Discourses

&

Mathematical Illustrations

pertaining to the

Extinction Shift Principle

under the Electrodynamics of Galilean Transformations

Edward Henry Dowdye, Jr.

West Chester, Pennsylvania
1991
Washington, DC
2001

on the

Mechanics of Propagation of Electromagnetic and Gravitational Fields and the Effect of their Influence on Fractional Light Velocity Particles of Material Secondary Sources of Emission

an Alternative to Doppler Shift and Relativistic Principles

with an Appendix on

Aberrational Effect, Sagnac Effect, Gravitational Redshift Effect and Nullified Experiments in Optics

Second Edition 2001

ISBN 0-9634471-4-9: Hardcover
ISBN 0-9634471-5-7: Softcover

Library of Congress Catalog Control Number: 2001116515

Second Edition 2001 **Second Printing 2001**

Edward Henry Dowdye, Jr.
P.O. Box 26023
Washington, DC 20001-6023

Author's Note

There is a simple, profound and overlooked classical alternative to Special and General Relativity principles. This alternative requires no assumptions other than those of *pure* classical physics and the most elementary mathematics. It is the *correct* alternative that uses only the mathematics and physics known at the time of the greatest scientists of all time, the great Galileo Galilei and the master of natural laws, Sir Isaac Newton. The alternative calculations lead directly to solutions to the physics of fractional light velocity problems encountered by the establishment of physical science during the last century. Until now, these problems were solvable only with the use of Relativity. I now invite the reader to put aside for the moment these non-classical tools which serve only as corrections to the incorrectly formulated principles of *natural law.* The reader can now use only the most elementary mathematics and classical approaches understandable to the new pupil of science, and experience, as I have, the beauty and truth of *undisturbed nature.*

In memory of

my grandmother, Mrs. Letha Cordell Rue,
and grandfather, Mr. Alonzo James Rue,

my father, Edward Henry Dowdye, V.M.D.

and

my uncle, Mr. James White, Esquire
to whom I am most indebted for the invaluable inspiration, wisdom
and technical craftsmanship imparted to me since the time of my youth

In dedication to

my mother

Rachelle Rue Richardson

and to

family and friends

and to

Miss Rosa Atmore, a memorable teacher

Acknowledgment

A special thanks to

Professor Emeritus Dr. Anne Baecker
for her invaluable support of my academic endeavors in Germany
and for her many kind and grateful deeds of encouragement and
helpful consultations

Many thanks to

Amy L. Ventura
for her orchestration of
the review process and publication
of the original manuscripts
of the First Edition

and to

Denise Ann Rich
Proofreader extra ordinaire

In memory of the

Late Professor and Friend, Dr. John A. Okolowski
Peer Reviewer of the First Edition

Theme of the Book

This book shows how the current establishment of physical science has successfully dictated to academia a model of laws of nature, **not** necessarily of the *true* laws of nature, dressing it up with principles and rules of convenience in order to force the theory to agree with the reality of observation and measurements born out of the experiment in the laboratory. Examples of such rules of convenience are the Lorentz transformations, the length contractions, the principle of time dilation of the clocks and the principle of velocity dependent masses. Ignored is the fact that there are certain occurrences in nature's laboratories that are simply denied observation to man. These are occurrences in nature which cannot be observed without causing direct interference, thus destroying the original, *true* character of the phenomenon under observation. Even the great Galileo Galilei {1564-1642} recognized this most important fact pertaining to the *true* law of nature. Observation introduces distortion by man's measurements.

The measurement in the laboratory cannot agree with any theory that employs incorrect principles to describe the physics of the *true* nature. If such principles become the orthodox rules and accepted practices of physical science, then the measured results will have to be corrected by employing **new** rules to correct the first. Einstein's Theory of Relativity serves only as a correction to the incorrect principles and accepted practices of the physics of today. It is the correction to the incorrectly formulated Doppler Shift Principle and all other principles pertaining to velocities that are a significant fraction of the velocity of light. It is the correction to the physics of the atomic particles that move with fractional light velocities in the high energy accelerators, the physics of the gravitational laws of planetary motion and the motion of the stars, such as the planet Mercury or the recently discovered PSR 1913+16 neutron-pulsar star system.

Supporters of Relativity claim that this theory is needed to solve all these problems. Yet, this book shows how Relativity is <u>not</u> needed by mathematically illustrating the solutions to these problems and all the other problems upon which the Theory of Relativity is based and claims its fame. The solutions are obtained with just a few lines of elementary mathematics and *pure* classical physics with **no** Relativity. The book shows proof that the physics text books are ignoring the most important principle of the physics of "*undisturbed*" nature. It is the principle this author calls the "*Extinction Shift Principle.*"

Contents

Discourses
&
Mathematical Illustrations
pertaining to the

Extinction Shift Principle

under Electrodynamics of

Galilean Transformations

Background and Issues

Since the time of Galileo Galilei {1564-1642 AD}, the established laws that govern nature and the universe have been molded only by a select few, the so called masters-of-the-trade, disciplined in their own fields and philosophical points of view. These too often became the accepted truth, the boundaries that constrained the necessary formulation of truisms to follow. The discipline of physical science contains many examples wherein concepts based on erroneous principles of the establishment were responsible for blocking the correct path to an alternative theory.

Nicolaus Copernicus {1473-1543}, about 100 years before the time of Galileo, put forth the idea that the earth and the other planets orbit about the sun and that the earth is not the center of the universe. Ironically, the forcing of Galileo[1] to recant his support of the Copernican Theory by the Inquisition of the Roman Catholic Church, is an *unheeded lesson* even to the establishment today. The views of many respected scientists and philosophers of the modern age of science are not accepted by the current establishment, even if their views and theories present an equally valid, if not better alternative to those of the current establishment. It is also ironic that the well founded laws of gravitation and of planetary motion found in the 'Philosophiae naturalis principia mathematica', a masterpiece by Sir Isaac Newton {1642-1727}, are found to be as valid as any modern theory when properly applied with alternative, classical treatments using solely elementary mathematics and classical physics. Of great value to Sir Isaac Newton were the laws of planetary motion derived by Johannes Kepler {1571-1630} and published in 1609 and 1619, decades before Newton. These very same laws, when used with an alternative, mathematical equivalence of the more modern and complex Special and General Relativistic principles, can be used, **without** resorting to relativistic treatments, to arrive at exactly the same results mathematically obtained **with** the use of modern relativistic treatments.

The key issue here is that of the *constancy of the velocity of light* in ideal vacuum in all frames of reference. Of primary importance are the principles and laws that were accepted by the establishment as universal physical laws and that are based on the *constancy of the velocity of light* theory. Since the failed experiment of Albert Michelson in 1881 and his repeat of the experiment with Edward Morley in 1887 of the so-called "interferometer ether drift" experiment,[2] the Relativity Theory of Albert Einstein {1879-1955} rose to fill a serious void in the discipline of physics. This void in the lack of a correct interpretation for the *apparent* constancy of the velocity of light, was due to the erroneously interpreted results of the Michelson-Morley experiment and its *misunderstood* significance to the theory of light.

The fatal error was simply that Michelson and Morley's failure to observe a shift in the optical fringe pattern resulted in the incorrect conclusion that the velocity of light did not change! However, the velocity of light can indeed change **without** affecting the observed frequency or phase to first order as would be exhibited by optical fringe shifts. Proof of this is given in the examples to follow by mathematically illustrating the alternative approaches to solutions of physical science problems, thought to be solvable only by using relativistic procedures. These include such problems as that of the perihelion rotation of the planet Mercury and of the recently discovered PSR1913+16 neutron-pulsar binary star system, claimed to be a modern test for the validity of Relativity. The calculations are accomplished using solely Galilean transformations and the rules of the *extinction shift principle*,[3] an alternative to the Doppler and other incorrectly formulated principles which always require relativistic corrections whenever significant fractions of the velocity of light are involved. Exact solutions to such problems, which the current establishment claims requires Special and General Relativity, can all be solved using elementary mathematics, *pure* classical physics and the *extinction shift principle* alone.

It follows immediately that, counter to established views, the wavelength of an *undisturbed* primary electromagnetic wave **cannot** shift according to the conventional definition of the Doppler shift principle. It is rather re-emitted as an *extinction shifted* wavelength of a secondary wave upon changing its velocity of propagation! As a consequence of the Galilean transformations, an *undisturbed* wavelength is independent of the reference frame. A similar theory known as the Ballistic Theory of Light was proposed by Wolfgang Pauli {1900-1958} who stated that the distance between bullets fired by a moving aircraft will remain unchanged to a fixed as well as to a moving observer. Similarly, the waves of electromagnetic radiation will propagate with *unchanged wavelengths* in an ideal vacuum and will be changed only at the measuring apparatus.

The *extinction shift principle* defines the rules and *principal axioms* for the correct method of applying the Galilean transformations and the laws of nature without the need of tweaking the scales of measurements or warping the units of universal time. As will be illustrated in the following examples of solved physics problems, it is found that the *extinction shift principle* applies universally to **all** radiation and fields; i.e., electromagnetic, electrostatic, magnetic and gravitational radiation and is valid under the electrodynamics of Galilean transformations.

Preface

The *extinction shift principle*, an alternative to the Doppler shift principle [4], is illustrated herein. An equivalent / alternative procedure to relativistic methods is given using solely the *extinction shift principle* and Galilean transformations. The equivalent alternative formulation makes use of no relativistic length contractions, time dilations or velocity dependent mass changes.

It is assumed that all fields, i.e., electric, magnetic, gravitational and electromagnetic fields, propagate with velocity c relative to the source of origin, and with velocity $c \pm v$ relative to an observer in a stationary frame if the source moves with the velocity $\pm v$ relative to the observer. Since the field is the vehicle by which force and energy are transmitted, then force and energy are assumed to propagate with the same velocity and are *extinction shifted* by means of the same principles employing Galilean electrodynamics.

Extinction Shift Principle: Graphical

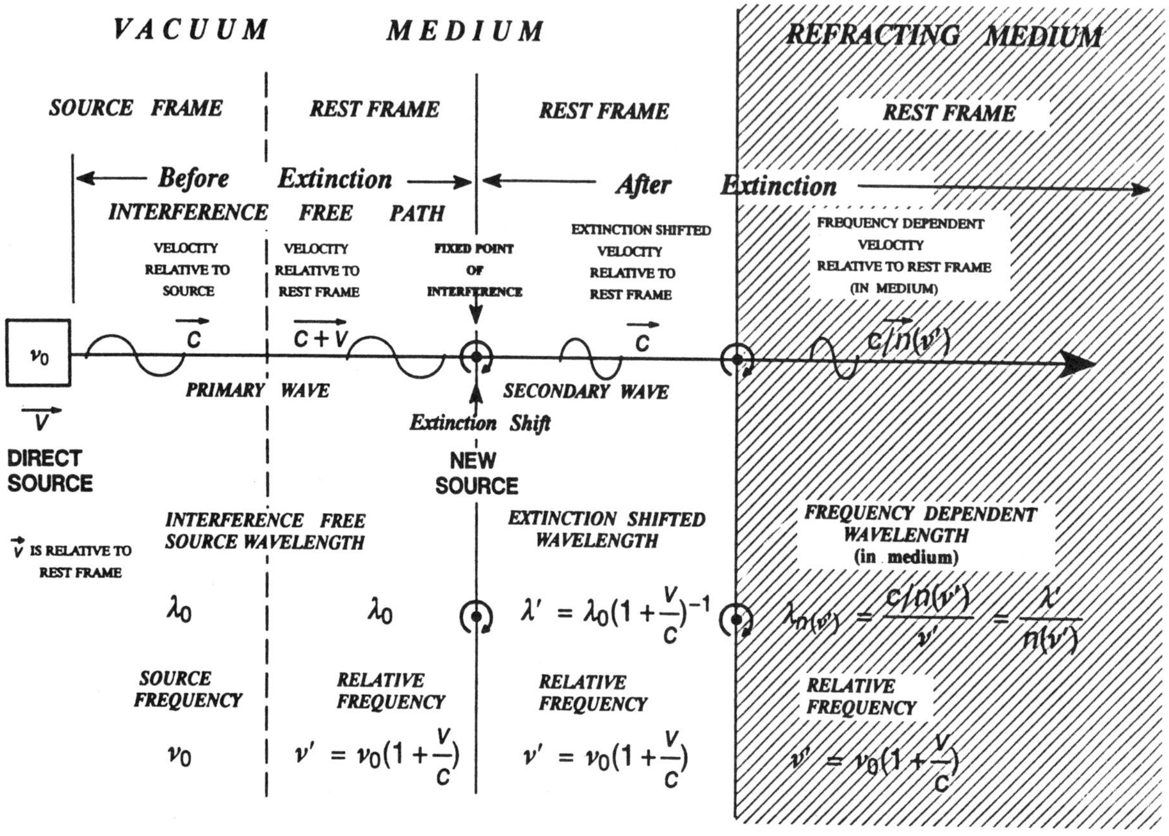

Vorwort

Es wird hiermit das Prinzip der *Löschverschiebung* { Auslöschen der Primärwelle + verschiebung der wiedergestrahlten Sekundärwelle }, eine Alternative zum Dopplerprinzip [4] , illustriert. Es wird ein äquivalentes, alternatives Verfahren zur relativistischen Methoden angegeben, welche anschließlich nur das *Löschverschiebungsprinzip* und die Galileitransformationen benutzt. Für die äquivalente, alternative Formulierung, werden von den Lorentzkontraktionen {Verkürzung der Maßstäbe}, der Zeitdilatation {Zeitverlangsammung} und der geschwindigkeitsabhängenden {relativistischen} Masse keinen Gebrauch gemacht.

Es wird angenommen, daß alle Felde, nämlich die elektrische, die magnetische, die elektromagnetische, sowie auch die Gravitationsfelde mit Lichtgeschwindigkeit c bezüglich der mit Geschwindigkeit $\pm v$ bewegten Quelle, aber mit der Geschwindigkeit $c \pm v$ relativ zum rehunden Beobachter fortpflanzen. Da das Feld selber das Mittel zum Transmission der Kraft and Energie ist, müßten auch die Kraft and die Energie mit der gleichen Geschwindigkeit fortpflanzen und auch im gleichem Sinne der Galilei–Elektrondynamik *löschverschoben* sein.

Löschverschiebungsprinzip: Graphische Darstellung

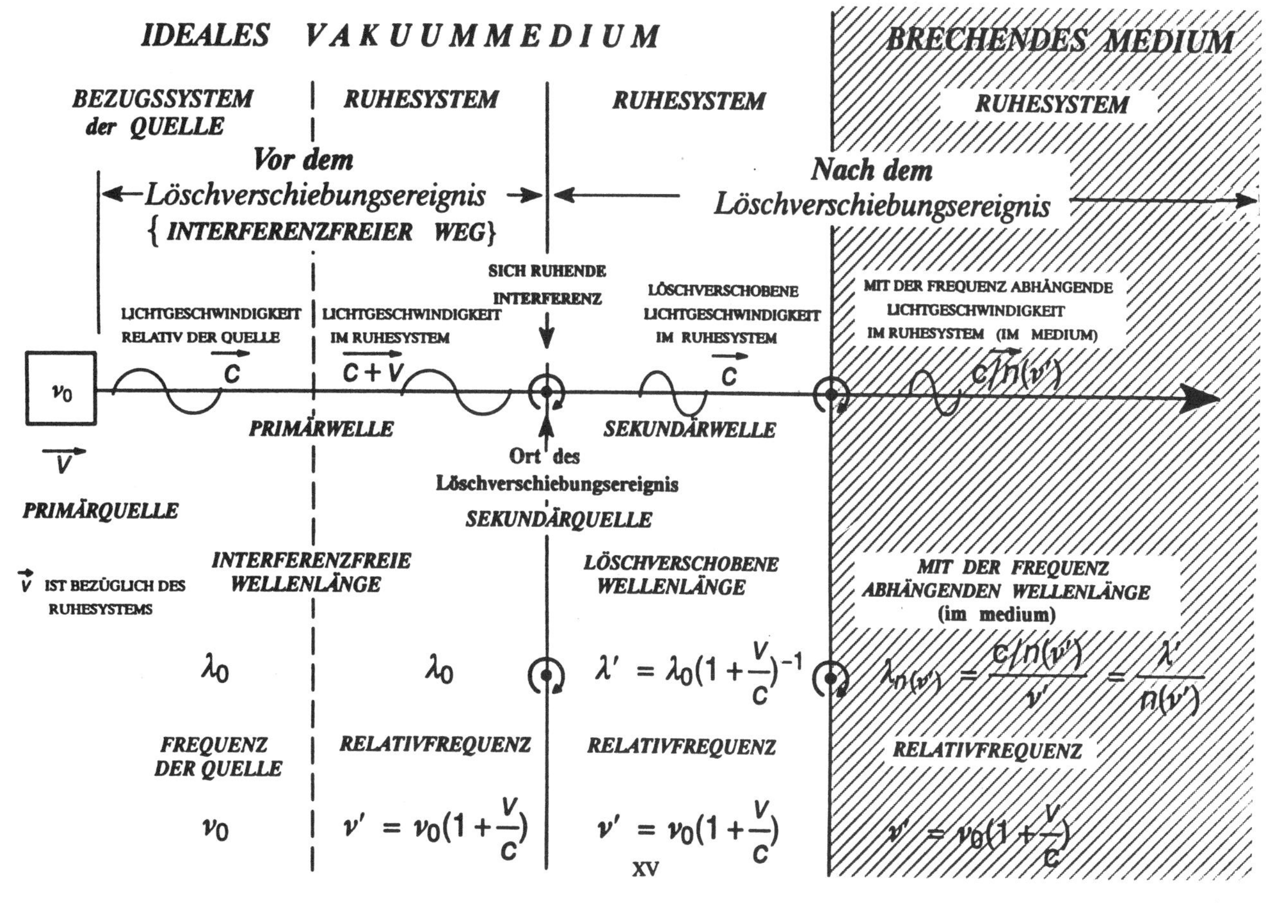

Introduction

It is illustrated herein that the Special and General Principles of Relativity are merely a mathematical equivalent to the correctly formulated ***natural laws***. The Relativity principles serve only as a correction to the incorrectly formulated principles of the physics of fractional light velocities supported by the current establishment. For instance, principles such as the Doppler shift incorrectly require that the velocity of propagation of electromagnetic waves and gravitation has to be constant in **all** frames of reference.

The correctly formulated extinction shift principle presented here requires **no** relativistic corrections, permitting one to arrive at precisely the same results using Galilean transformations and elementary mathematics **without** Relativity. The *extinction shift principle* defines the rules for applying the transformations and the mathematics. It is the correct formulation of the physics involving the electrodynamics of fractional light velocities without Relativity.

Mathematical illustrations of the *extinction shift principle* are:

- The Invariance of the Wave Equation using solely the principal axioms of the *extinction shift principles* under Galilean transformations applied to re-emissions in Euclidean Space Geometry
- Various optical gyroscopes using the *extinction shift principles* as defined on page 14, in reference [4] and Appendix II, illustrating the Sagnac effect
- A typical problem in convection of waves in a moving refracting medium, where an equivalence to a frequency dependent index of refraction is understood
- A problem of a moving charged mass under influence of an accelerating potential, yielding an equivalent *effective* mass $m_{eff} = m_0 / \sqrt{1 - \frac{v^2}{c^2}}$, the mathematical equivalence to the relativistic mass
- A *transverse relative time shift* which is a direct consequence of *extinction shifting* and re-emissions between frames of reference, yielding $\tau_{tr} = \tau_0 / \sqrt{1 - \frac{v^2}{c^2}}$ a ***pure*** classical equivalence to the *Time Dilation*
- A ***pure*** classical solution to the Mercury perihelion rotation problem, yielding 42.998 arcsec/century, from Galilean transformations of the gravitational effects of interacting mass particles in Euclidean space
- A ***pure*** classical solution to the PSR1913+16 binary pulsar perihelion rotation, yielding 4.2265 degrees/year, the precise result of Relativity
- The Appendix includes ***pure*** classical solutions to Gravitational Redshift and Solar Light Bending effects obtaining $\Delta\nu = \nu_0 \frac{GM}{Rc^2}$ and $\delta\theta = \frac{4GM}{Rc^2}$, respectively, using solely the *extinction shift principle* and Galilean transformations on the rectilinear path of photons re-emitted from secondary sources of emission.

Extinction Shift Principle Illustrated; Some Classical Alternatives equivalent to Special and General Relativistic Principles

Definition of Extinction Shift

Any wavelength λ_0 and frequency ν_0 of *primary* electromagnetic radiation will propagate along an interference free path with velocity c relative to its most *DIRECT* source which moves with velocity v_1 and with velocity $c + v_1$ relative to the rest frame. The *undisturbed* wavelength will remain unchanged {*preserved in all other frames of reference*}, along an interference-free path, independent of the source velocity. [3]

Upon interference, the *primary* wave is extinguished via a matter-wave interaction, thus terminating the interference-free path at the point of interference, or at a SECONDARY source moving with velocity v_2. Any *secondary* wave would be re-emitted on the frequency $\nu' = \nu_0(1 + \frac{v_1 - v_2}{c})$ as would be noted in the frame of reference of the *secondary* source, moving with velocity v_2. The re-emitted, *secondary* wave will have the *undisturbed* wavelength $\lambda' = \frac{c}{\nu'} = \lambda_0(1 + \frac{v_1 - v_2}{c})^{-1}$ {*preserved in all frames*} and will propagate along an interference free path with velocity c relative to the SECONDARY source and with velocity $c + v_2$ relative to the rest frame. [3]

Upon interference, thus terminating the interference-free path of the *secondary* wave, at the point of interference, or at the TERTIARY source moving with velocity v_3, a *tertiary* wave would be re-emitted on the frequency $\nu'' = \nu'(1 + \frac{v_2 - v_3}{c}) = \nu_0(1 + \frac{v_1 - v_2}{c})(1 + \frac{v_2 - v_3}{c})$ as would be noted in the frame of reference of the *tertiary* source, moving with velocity v_3. The re-emitted, *tertiary* wave will have the *undisturbed* wavelength $\lambda'' = \frac{c}{\nu''} = \lambda_0(1 + \frac{v_1 - v_2}{c})^{-1}(1 + \frac{v_2 - v_3}{c})^{-1}$ {*preserved in all frames*} propagating along an interference free path with velocity c relative to the TERTIARY source and with velocity $c + v_3$ relative to the rest frame. [3]

Similarly, any N-ary wave will be re-emitted with velocity c relative to its N-ary source of velocity v_N and will propagate with *undisturbed* velocity $c + v_N$ relative to the rest frame.

Extinction Shift Principle Illustrated; Some Classical Alternatives equivalent to Special and General Relativistic Principles

Definition of Extinction Shift (Continued)

A hypothetical observer, moving with velocity v_0, able to observe ALL events without interference, would note the undisturbed velocities $c + v_1 - v_0$, $c + v_2 - v_0$ and $c + v_3 - v_0$ and the undisturbed wavelengths λ_0, $\lambda' = \lambda_0(1 + \frac{v_1 - v_2}{c})^{-1}$ and $\lambda'' = \lambda_0(1 + \frac{v_1 - v_2}{c})^{-1}(1 + \frac{v_2 - v_3}{c})^{-1}$ of the DIRECT, SECONDARY and TERTIARY sources, respectively.

Any ordinary observer, moving with velocity v_0, would note the frequencies

$\nu_0(1 + \frac{v_1 - v_0}{c})$ for the direct,

$\nu'(1 + \frac{v_2 - v_0}{c}) = [\nu_0(1 + \frac{v_1 - v_2}{c})](1 + \frac{v_2 - v_0}{c})$ for the secondary and

$\nu''(1 + \frac{v_3 - v_0}{c}) = [\nu_0(1 + \frac{v_1 - v_2}{c})(1 + \frac{v_2 - v_3}{c})](1 + \frac{v_3 - v_0}{c})$ for the tertiary source. [3]

Note: The *undisturbed* wavelengths are independent of any reference frame. Neither the *undisturbed* velocities nor the *undisturbed* wavelengths are measurable by ordinary means! A measurement on the wavelengths would yield in all cases

$\lambda_0(1 + \frac{v_1 - v_0}{c})^{-1}$ for the direct,

$\lambda'(1 + \frac{v_2 - v_0}{c})^{-1}$ for the secondary and

$\lambda''(1 + \frac{v_3 - v_0}{c})^{-1}$ for the tertiary source,

to any *ordinary* observer moving with velocity v_0. To any fixed observer $\{ v_0 = 0 \}$

$\lambda_0(1 + \frac{v_1}{c})^{-1}$ for the direct,

$\lambda'(1 + \frac{v_2}{c})^{-1}$ for the secondary and

$\lambda''(1 + \frac{v_3}{c})^{-1}$ for the tertiary and similarly for any N–ary source are noted.

Here, the ordinary, real–world observer is the equivalent of the hypothetical observer with a window placed in front of him, in his frame of reference.

The fixed hypothetical observer here would note that the interference would *not* change the velocity–to–wavelength ratio of the radiation. Consequently, in a fixed observer's frame of reference, the relative frequency ν' of the *primary* radiation noted *before interference* would always equal the relative frequency of the *secondary* radiation noted *after interference*. [3]

Extinction Shift Principle Illustrated; Some Classical Alternatives equivalent to Special and General Relativity Principles

Definition of Extinction Shift applied to Gravitation

Any interaction between two mass particles in the same frame of reference and separated by space and a distance r between them will occur with a characteristic one-way transit time of $\tau_{one-way} = \frac{r}{c}$, where c is the velocity of propagation of the gravitation field relative to its primary source, the mass particle setting it up. The round trip transit time is thus $\tau_{round-trip} = \frac{2r}{c}$. The round-trip transit time between any two mass particles approaching one another with the relative velocity v is $\tau_{round-trip} = \frac{2r}{c+v}$. The round-trip transit time between any two mass particles receding one another with the relative velocity v is $\tau_{round-trip} = \frac{2r}{c-v}$.

In general, the round-trip transit time between two approaching masses is $\tau_{round-trip} = \frac{2r}{c'_{app}}$. $c'_{app} = \sqrt{c^2 + v^2 - 2cvCos\phi}$ is the vector sum of the velocities c and v. ϕ is the angle between the line joining the masses and the relative directions of motion of the approaching masses. Similarly, $\tau_{round-trip} = \frac{2r}{c'_{rec}}$, where $c'_{rec} = \sqrt{c^2 - v^2 + 2cvCos\phi}$ is the vector sum of the velocities c and v for receding masses. Any gravitational signal conveyed from one mass to another approaching/receding mass would have a decreased/increased transit time or an effective decreased / increased transit distance of $r_{app} = (\frac{c}{c'_{app}})r$ / $r_{rec} = (\frac{c}{c'_{rec}})r$.

A *primary* gravitational wave conveys information on its most DIRECT source, say a mass particle **M**, with velocity c relative to **M** which moves with velocity v_1 relative to the rest frame. Assume this *primary* wave has a wavelength λ_0 and moves with velocity $c + v_1$ relative to the rest frame, analogous to the case of electromagnetism. It would have the velocity $c + v_1 - v_2$ relative to a particle **m** of velocity v_2, perturbing it and causing it to wiggle at the frequency $\nu' = \frac{c+v_1-v_2}{\lambda_0} = \nu_0(1 + \frac{v_1-v_2}{c})$. The gravitational field set up by **m** would convey indirect information on **M** at the wavelength $\lambda' = \frac{c}{\nu'} = \lambda_0(1 + \frac{v_1-v_2}{c})^{-1}$, propagating with velocity c relative to **m** and with velocity $c + v_2$ relative to the rest frame.

Herewith, the very same principal axioms are applicable to both gravitation and electromagnetism.

Discourses

&

Mathematical Illustrations

pertaining to the

Extinction Shift Principle

under Electrodynamics of

Galilean Transformations

Extinction Shift Principle Illustrated; Some Classical Alternatives equivalent to Special and General Relativity Principles

On Invariance of the Wave Equation $\frac{\partial^2\Phi}{\partial x^2} + \frac{\partial^2\Phi}{\partial y^2} + \frac{\partial^2\Phi}{\partial z^2} - \frac{1}{c^2}\frac{\partial^2\Phi}{\partial t^2} = 0$ under Electrodynamics of Galilean Transformations, using the Principal Axioms of the *Extinction Shift Principle* applied to Re-emission in Euclidean Space Geometry

Assume:

i) All *undisturbed* primary waves, i.e., $\Phi = \Phi_0 Sin 2\pi(\nu t + \frac{1}{\lambda}x)$ are emitted at velocity c relative to their most *primary* sources and upon any interference are then re-emitted at the same velocity c in the frame of reference of the interference. The *undisturbed* primary wave propagates with velocity $c' \neq c$ in all frames of reference other than that of the most primary source. The re-emitted *secondary* wave $\Phi' = \Phi'_0 Sin 2\pi(\nu' t' + \frac{1}{\lambda'}x')$ noted with relative frequency ν' and *extinction shifted* wavelength λ', propagates with velocity c relative to its secondary source.[3]

ii) The *undisturbed* (not measurable) wavelength λ, void of interference, remains unchanged in all frames of reference.

iii) The laws governing emission and re-emission do **not** change with the frame of reference.

As a consequence of i, ii and iii, the apparent equations of motion, due to measurement or *extinction* of the primary wave, will be the same for all observers, regardless of the frame of reference, since the velocity of the re-emitted wave is always c in the frame of reference of the interference. Only the *observed* frequency ν' and *extinction shifted* wavelength λ' will depend on the frame of reference. From the principal axioms of the *Extinction Shift Principle* (See Appendix IV), all interfering observers will measure a frequency ν' and a wavelength λ', the product of which is always c. In the frame of reference of the primary source, $\nu\lambda = c$. For any approaching source, the observable is always $\nu'\lambda' = [\nu(1+\frac{v}{c})][\lambda(1+\frac{v}{c})^{-1}] = \nu\lambda = c$. For any receding source, the observable is always $\nu'\lambda' = [\nu(1-\frac{v}{c})][\lambda(1-\frac{v}{c})^{-1}] = \nu\lambda = c$.

A *hypothetical*, non-interfering observer, however, would note that the velocity of the *undisturbed* wave would depend on the reference frame, strictly obeying Galilean transformations and that the *undisturbed* wavelength λ, **not** measurable by any interfering observer, would remain unchanged!

The *hypothetical* observer, who abides strictly by the principal axioms of the *Extinction Shift Principle*, while correctly applying these rules to Galilean transformation in Euclidean Space Geometry, would correctly predict that all interfering observers would always note $\nu'\lambda' = \nu\lambda = c$. By differentiating the equation $\Phi' = \Phi'_0 Sin 2\pi(\nu' t' + \frac{1}{\lambda'}x')$ twice after t' and x', the interfering observer arrives at $\frac{\partial^2\Phi'}{\partial t'^2} = -\Phi'(2\pi)^2\nu'^2 = \nu'^2\lambda'^2\frac{\partial^2\Phi'}{\partial x'^2}$. Thus, the interfering observer, regardless of his frame of reference, derives the same equation $\frac{\partial^2\Phi'}{\partial x'^2} + \frac{\partial^2\Phi'}{\partial y'^2} + \frac{\partial^2\Phi'}{\partial z'^2} - \frac{1}{\nu'^2\lambda'^2}\frac{\partial^2\Phi'}{\partial t'^2} = 0$, for quantities differing only in ν' and λ', but not in $\nu'\lambda' = \nu\lambda = c$.

Herewith, the wave equation is found to be totally invariant under Galilean Transformations, using the correctly formulated principle axioms of the *Extinction Shift Principle*, applied to re-emissions in Euclidean Space Geometry.

On optical gyroscopes, Sagnac effect and rectilinear path of photons from re-emitters in rotating frames

In **Figure** 1, the frequency perceived at the 3–point re–emitters A, B and C is ν_0 to any observer in the respective frames of reference of the re–emitters. This is thereby consistent with the fact that the re–emitters have no relative motion with one another since they are rigidly attached to the rotating platform. However, a fixed observer with velocity $V_0 = 0$ positioned anywhere between any two of the re–emitters sampling the beams will note the frequency $\nu_0(1 + \frac{V_0 + V}{c})$ where the velocity $V = +\frac{1}{2}\omega r$ for the beam propagating with velocity $c + V$, and the corresponding frequency for velocity $V = -\frac{1}{2}\omega r$ for the opposing beam propagating with velocity $c - V$. The two frequencies noted by the fixed observer are $\nu_1 = \nu_0(1 + \frac{0 + \frac{1}{2}\omega r}{c})$ and $\nu_2 = \nu_0(1 + \frac{0 - \frac{1}{2}\omega r}{c})$ and thus the shift in frequency noted here and anywhere in the loop as seen from an inertial frame is $\Delta\nu = \nu_1 - \nu_2 = \nu_0 \frac{\omega r}{c}$.

Given that the ratio of area to length is $\frac{A}{L} = \frac{r}{4}$, the frequency shift is found to be $\Delta\nu = \frac{4A}{Lc}\omega\,\nu_0 = \frac{4A}{L\lambda}\omega$ for the 3–point re–emitter problem.

Assume that the point re–emitters are fed by a source located at the center of rotation of the optical gyros. Thus, for a fixed observer, the reference frequency noted directly from the source when compared with the frequency of any of the re–emitters will be equal only at the instant in time when the observed re–emitter is moving transversely with respect to the observer. As conveyed to any observer in an inertial frame by a sensor rotating with the frame, the difference in the loop frequency is always $\Delta\nu = \frac{4A}{L\lambda}\omega$.

It is shown in **Figures** 1 though 5 that this frequency shift $\Delta\nu = \frac{4A}{L\lambda}\omega$ is derivable for any value of N re–emitters or a multiple (N–point) system of N–ary emitters.

Optical Gyroscope: 3 Point Emitters

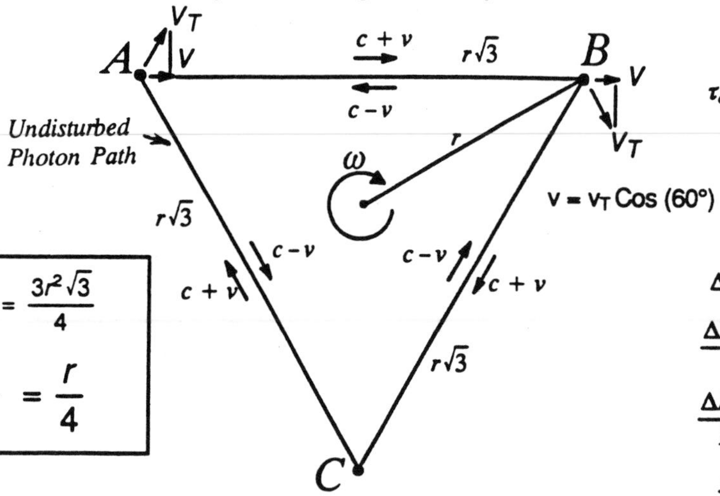

$$L = 3r\sqrt{3}$$

$$\tau_{c+v} = \frac{3r\sqrt{3}}{(c+v)-v} = \frac{3r\sqrt{3}}{c}$$

$$v_T = \omega r$$

$$v = \frac{v_T}{2} = \frac{\omega r}{2}$$

$$\Delta L_{c+v} = v\tau_{c+v} = \frac{3\sqrt{3}r^2}{2c}\omega$$

$$\frac{\Delta L_{c+v}}{L} = \frac{r}{2c}\omega = \frac{1}{2}\left(\frac{4A}{cL}\right)\omega$$

$$\frac{\Delta L_{c-v}}{L} = \frac{r}{2c}\omega = \frac{1}{2}\left(\frac{4A}{cL}\right)\omega$$

$$\frac{\Delta L}{L} = \frac{\Delta L_{c+v}}{L} + \frac{\Delta L_{c-v}}{L} = \frac{4A}{cL}\omega$$

$$A = \frac{3r^2\sqrt{3}}{4} \qquad \frac{A}{L} = \frac{r}{4}$$

$$\frac{\Delta L}{L} = \frac{\Delta\lambda}{\lambda} = \frac{\Delta\nu}{\nu} \qquad \Delta\nu = \frac{4A}{cL}\omega\nu = \frac{4A}{L\lambda}\omega$$

Figure 1

Optical Gyroscope: 4 Point Emitters

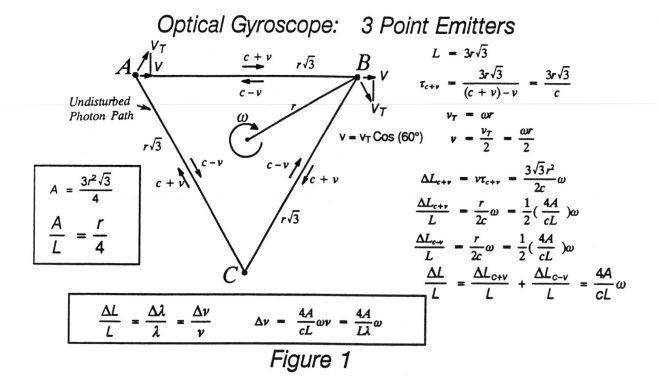

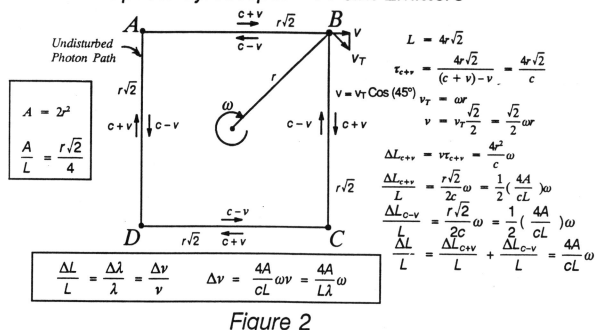

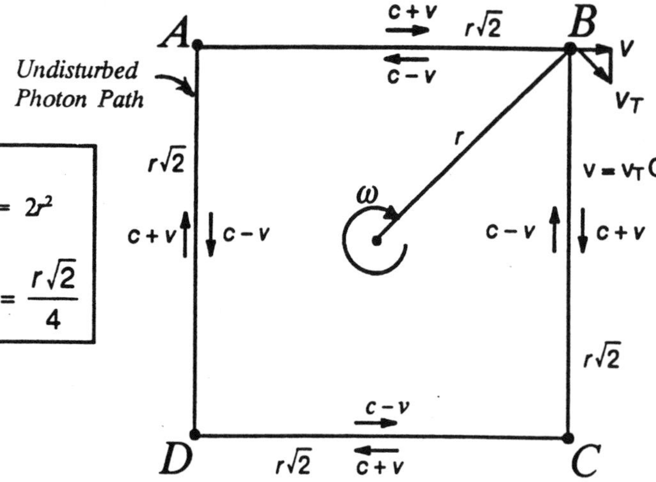

$$L = 4r\sqrt{2}$$

$$\tau_{c+v} = \frac{4r\sqrt{2}}{(c+v)-v} = \frac{4r\sqrt{2}}{c}$$

$$v_T = \omega r$$

$$v = v_T\frac{\sqrt{2}}{2} = \frac{\sqrt{2}}{2}\omega r$$

$$\Delta L_{c+v} = v\tau_{c+v} = \frac{4r^2}{c}\omega$$

$$\frac{\Delta L_{c+v}}{L} = \frac{r\sqrt{2}}{2c}\omega = \frac{1}{2}\left(\frac{4A}{cL}\right)\omega$$

$$\frac{\Delta L_{c-v}}{L} = \frac{r\sqrt{2}}{2c}\omega = \frac{1}{2}\left(\frac{4A}{cL}\right)\omega$$

$$\frac{\Delta L}{L} = \frac{\Delta L_{c+v}}{L} + \frac{\Delta L_{c-v}}{L} = \frac{4A}{cL}\omega$$

$$A = 2r^2 \qquad \frac{A}{L} = \frac{r\sqrt{2}}{4}$$

$$\frac{\Delta L}{L} = \frac{\Delta\lambda}{\lambda} = \frac{\Delta\nu}{\nu} \qquad \Delta\nu = \frac{4A}{cL}\omega\nu = \frac{4A}{L\lambda}\omega$$

Figure 2

Optical Gyroscope: 6 Point Emitters

$$A = \frac{3r^2\sqrt{3}}{2} \qquad \frac{A}{L} = \frac{r\sqrt{3}}{4}$$

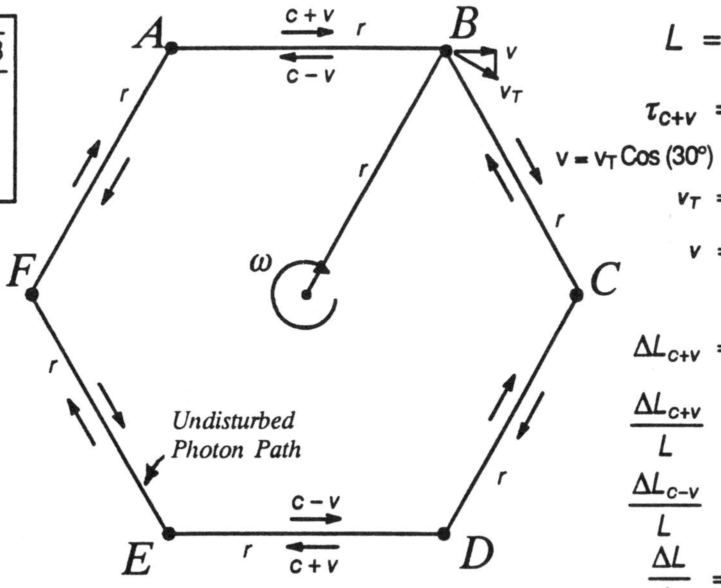

$$L = 6r$$

$$\tau_{c+v} = \frac{6r}{(c+v)-v} = \frac{6r}{c}$$

$$v_T = \omega r$$

$$v = v_T\frac{\sqrt{3}}{2} = \frac{\sqrt{3}}{2}\omega r$$

$$\Delta L_{c+v} = v\tau_{c+v} = \frac{3\sqrt{3}r^2}{c}\omega$$

$$\frac{\Delta L_{c+v}}{L} = \frac{r\sqrt{3}}{2c}\omega = \frac{1}{2}\left(\frac{4A}{cL}\right)\omega$$

$$\frac{\Delta L_{c-v}}{L} = \frac{r\sqrt{3}}{2c}\omega = \frac{1}{2}\left(\frac{4A}{cL}\right)\omega$$

$$\frac{\Delta L}{L} = \frac{\Delta L_{c+v}}{L} + \frac{\Delta L_{c-v}}{L} = \frac{4A}{cL}\omega$$

$$\frac{\Delta L}{L} = \frac{\Delta\lambda}{\lambda} = \frac{\Delta\nu}{\nu} \qquad \Delta\nu = \frac{4A}{cL}\omega\nu = \frac{4A}{L\lambda}\omega$$

Figure 3

Optical Gyroscope: N Point Emitters { N=large}

$$A = \pi r^2 \qquad \frac{A}{L} = \frac{r}{2}$$

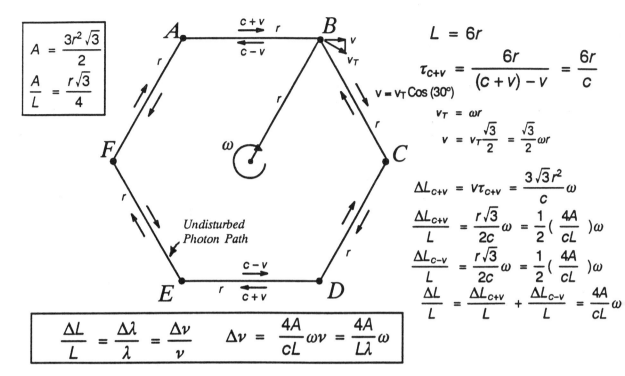

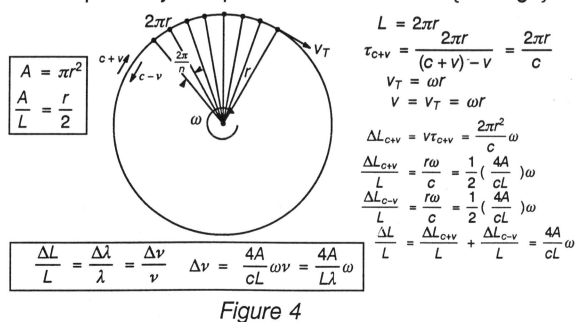

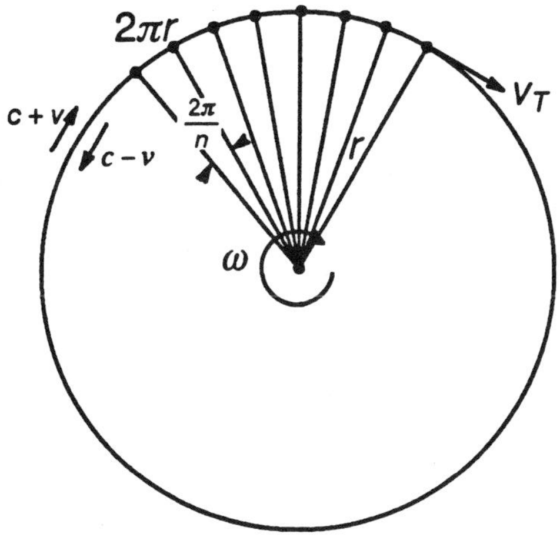

$$L = 2\pi r$$

$$\tau_{c+v} = \frac{2\pi r}{(c+v)-v} = \frac{2\pi r}{c}$$

$$v_T = \omega r$$

$$v = v_T = \omega r$$

$$\Delta L_{c+v} = v\tau_{c+v} = \frac{2\pi r^2}{c}\omega$$

$$\frac{\Delta L_{c+v}}{L} = \frac{r\omega}{c} = \frac{1}{2}\left(\frac{4A}{cL}\right)\omega$$

$$\frac{\Delta L_{c-v}}{L} = \frac{r\omega}{c} = \frac{1}{2}\left(\frac{4A}{cL}\right)\omega$$

$$\frac{\Delta L}{L} = \frac{\Delta L_{c+v}}{L} + \frac{\Delta L_{c-v}}{L} = \frac{4A}{cL}\omega$$

$$\frac{\Delta L}{L} = \frac{\Delta\lambda}{\lambda} = \frac{\Delta\nu}{\nu} \qquad \Delta\nu = \frac{4A}{cL}\omega\nu = \frac{4A}{L\lambda}\omega$$

Figure 4

Extinction Shift Principle Illustrated; Some Classical Alternatives equivalent to Special and General Relativistic Principles

In **Figures** 2, 3 and 4 the procedure used in **Figure** 1 is repeated, deriving the equivalent time–of–flight, the effective propagation length using Galilean transformations. In **Figure** 5, it is shown that an equivalence of the effective length for a refracting medium can be accomplished simply by letting the number of re–emitters in the loop $N \rightarrow \infty$. The ratio of the frequency dependent effective length to the actual length $L_N(\nu) / L$ replaces the index of refraction $n(\nu)$. $L_N(\nu)$ is the effective path length at the frequency of interference ν , $\Delta L_N(\nu)$ is the change in effective path length. It is shown that the ratio $\Delta L_N(\nu) / L_N(\nu)$ is actually $\frac{4A}{cL}\omega$, L being the actual physical length of the loop. This concept illustrates that the *extinction shift principle* is also applicable in refracting media as well as in vacuum.

Alternatively, it may be assumed that all electromagnetic radiation, electrostatic, magnetic and gravitational fields propagate with velocity c with respect to the most immediate *primary source*, i.e., with velocity c with respect to its N–ary re–emitter or the dipole element "N" of the medium whose velocity is v_N, but with velocity $c + v_N$ with respect to the rest frame. This velocity is *effectively* $c_n = \frac{c}{n(\nu)}$, characteristic of the refracting medium of index of refraction $n(\nu)$ at the frequency of interference ν , in the frame of the medium.

This re-emission process occurs universally, even in the most dense media! And there is **not** a shred of evidence against this.

Optical Gyroscope: Refracting Medium

Medium with Index of Refraction n with N re–emitters
N=Very Large

Since $n(\nu)$ is frequency dependent, then the *effective* velocity of the field in the medium is

$$c_n + v = c_n + v\left(1 - \frac{1}{n(\nu_0)^2} \cdot \frac{\partial n(\nu)}{\partial \nu}\,\nu_0\right),$$ essentially a Galilean transformation.

For all practical purposes, the effect contributed by the term $v\left(\frac{1}{n(\nu_0)^2} \cdot \frac{\partial n(\nu)}{\partial \nu}\nu_0\right)$ to any changes in the velocity in the medium is essentially a second order effect and can be neglected here.

See Page 17 on convection.

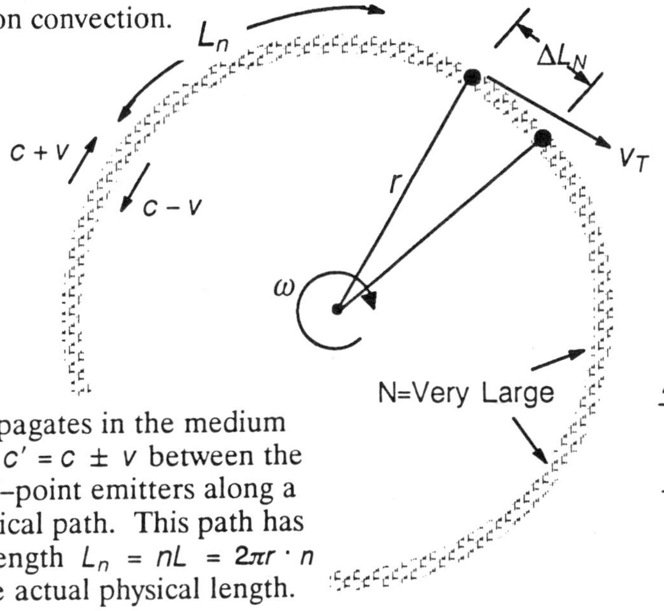

$$A = \pi r^2$$

$$\frac{A}{L} = \frac{r}{2}$$

$$L_n = 2\pi r \cdot n$$

$$\tau_{c+v} = \frac{L_n}{(c+v)-v} = \frac{L_n}{c}$$

$$V_T = \omega r$$

$$v = V_T = \omega r$$

$$\Delta L_{c+v} = v\tau_{c+v} = \frac{L_n}{c}\omega r$$

$$\frac{\Delta L_{c+v}}{L_n} = \frac{r\omega}{c} = \frac{1}{2}\left(\frac{4A}{cL}\right)\omega$$

$$\frac{\Delta L_{c-v}}{L_n} = \frac{r\omega}{c} = \frac{1}{2}\left(\frac{4A}{cL}\right)\omega$$

$$\frac{\Delta L_N}{L_n} = \frac{\Delta L_{c+v}}{L_n} + \frac{\Delta L_{c-v}}{L_n} = \frac{4A}{cL}\omega$$

The field propagates in the medium with velocity $c' = c \pm v$ between the constituent N–point emitters along a preferred optical path. This path has an effective length $L_n = nL = 2\pi r \cdot n$ Here, L is the actual physical length.

$$\frac{\Delta L_N}{L_N} = \frac{\Delta L}{L} = \frac{\Delta\lambda_n}{\lambda_n} = \frac{\Delta\lambda}{\lambda} = \frac{\Delta\nu}{\nu} \qquad \Delta\nu = \frac{4A}{cL}\omega\nu = \frac{4A}{L\lambda}\omega$$

$$\Delta\nu = \frac{4A}{L\lambda}\omega$$

The wave propagates in the medium with effective velocity c_n and wavelength λ_n and has the vacuum wavelength $\lambda = n\lambda_n$. The effective length along the optical path is nL for field of velocity c relative to the finite number of N–point emitters. The area A has no physical importance other than convenience for the mathematical expression of the effect! $A \,/\, L$ is the ratio of the physical area to actual length.

Figure 5

Sagnac Effect Explained using Extinction Shift Principle

In **Figure** 6 and 7 the source and observer are rigidly attached to the rotating platform. A phase shift as function of the angular velocity ω is noted.

In **Figure** 6, the frequency perceived at the re–emitters A, B and C and at the screen S is ν_0 to an observer in the respective frames of reference. This perception is thereby consistent with the fact that the re–emitters and the screen have no relative motion with one another since they are rigidly attached to the rotating platform. See Appendix II: Sagnac Effect (Proof of Galilean Transformation)

The screen moves the distance ΔX during the transit time of the light around the loop SCBAS and the change in path ΔL for the loop is simply $\Delta X\sqrt{2}/2$ in the direction of the re–emitter points. The propagation of all radiation is one of a rectilinear motion, along a straight line. Thus, the frame does *not* rotate with the platform and the distance between the re–emitter points is constant. As a consequence of rectilinear motion of radiation and the Galilean transformation, the path length is *not* constant! It is shown that the shift due to change in propagation path length is $\Delta\phi = \frac{4A}{c\lambda}\omega$ which is derivable for any value of N for a system of multiple N–point or N–ary re–emitters {number of dipole antenna elements re–emitting the wave in the refracting medium}.

Sagnac Effect Explained using Extinction Shift Principle

Optical Rotational Sensor: 4 Point Emitters

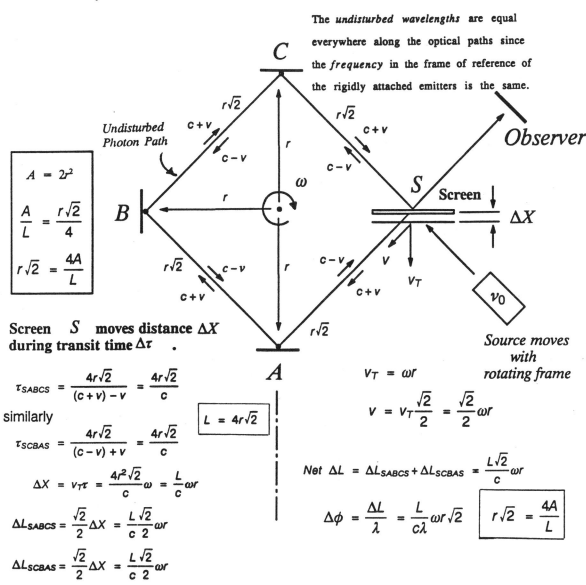

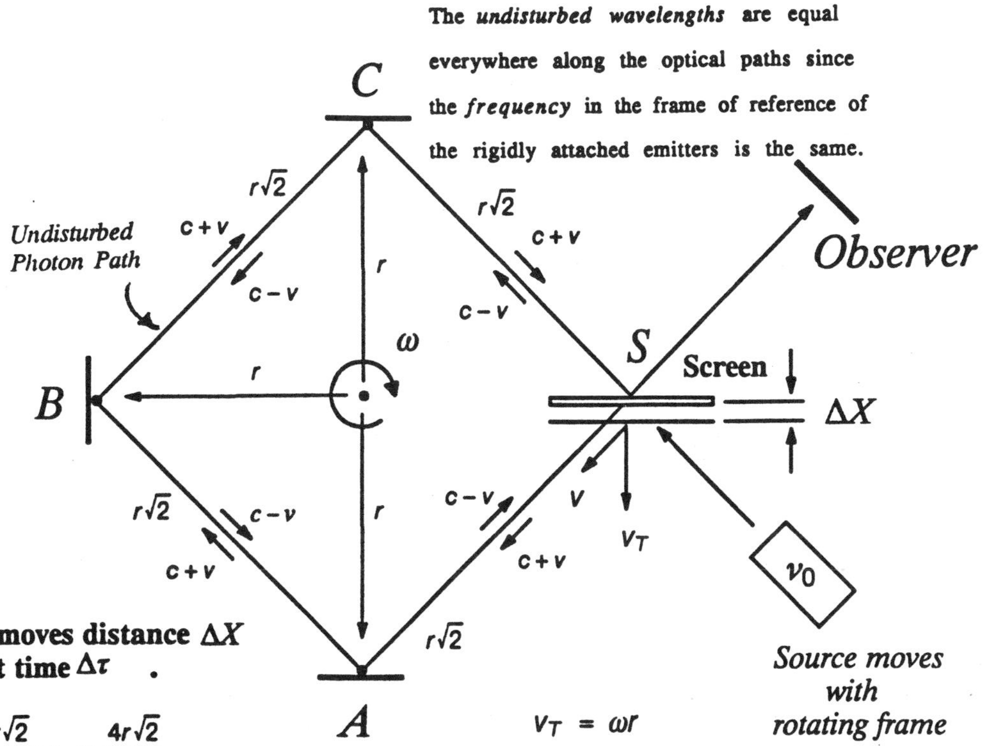

$$A = 2r^2$$

$$\frac{A}{L} = \frac{r\sqrt{2}}{4}$$

$$r\sqrt{2} = \frac{4A}{L}$$

Screen S moves distance ΔX during transit time $\Delta\tau$.

$$V_T = \omega r$$

$$V = V_T\frac{\sqrt{2}}{2} = \frac{\sqrt{2}}{2}\omega r$$

$$\tau_{SABCS} = \frac{4r\sqrt{2}}{(c+v)-v} = \frac{4r\sqrt{2}}{c}$$

similarly

$$L = 4r\sqrt{2}$$

$$\tau_{SCBAS} = \frac{4r\sqrt{2}}{(c-v)+v} = \frac{4r\sqrt{2}}{c}$$

$$\Delta X = v_T\tau = \frac{4r^2\sqrt{2}}{c}\omega = \frac{L}{c}\omega r$$

$$\Delta L_{SABCS} = \frac{\sqrt{2}}{2}\Delta X = \frac{L}{c}\frac{\sqrt{2}}{2}\omega r$$

$$\Delta L_{SCBAS} = \frac{\sqrt{2}}{2}\Delta X = \frac{L}{c}\frac{\sqrt{2}}{2}\omega r$$

$$\text{Net } \Delta L = \Delta L_{SABCS} + \Delta L_{SCBAS} = \frac{L\sqrt{2}}{c}\omega r$$

$$\Delta\phi = \frac{\Delta L}{\lambda} = \frac{L}{c\lambda}\omega r\sqrt{2} \qquad r\sqrt{2} = \frac{4A}{L}$$

Phase Shift Noted

$$\Delta\phi = \frac{4A}{c\lambda}\omega$$

Figure 6

Sagnac Effect Explained using Extinction Shift Principle

Optical Rotational Sensor: N–Point Emitters {N=large}

Optical Fiber

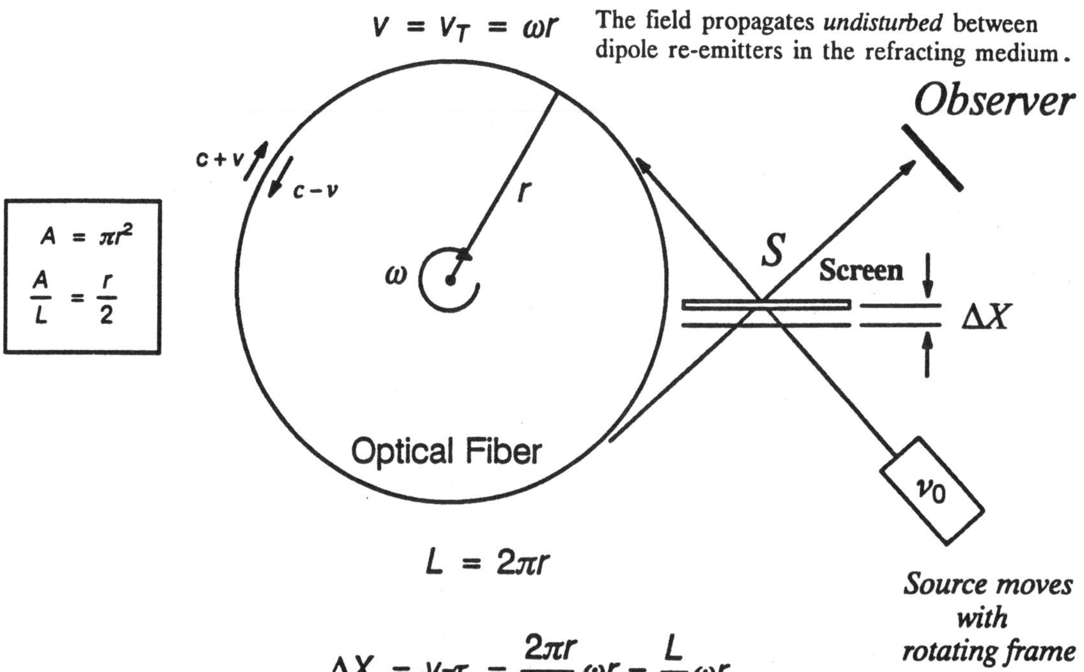

$$\Delta X = v_T \tau = \frac{2\pi r}{c}\,\omega r = \frac{L}{c}\,\omega r$$

The field in the fiber is re-emitted with velocity **c** relative to its most N-ary source *effectively* along the length of the fiber since N=large. Therefore $\Delta L = \Delta X$. ΔL is actually the accumulative of δ_N of the N path changes between the re-emitters.

Phase Shift Noted

$$\Delta\phi = \frac{\Delta L}{\lambda} = \frac{2L}{c\lambda}\omega r \qquad r = \frac{2A}{L} \qquad \longrightarrow \qquad \Delta\phi = \frac{4A}{c\lambda}\omega$$

See Appendix II: Sagnac Effect (Proof of Galilean Transformation), Page 6A

Figure 7

On convection of waves in moving media of dipole secondary sources of emission

In **Figures** 8 and 9, using as a tool a *hypothetical* observer capable of observing without interference the wave in vacuum and in the medium, it is shown that an equivalent formulation can be obtained for the so–called Fresnel dragging effect noted in refracting media. The index of refraction $n(\nu)$ expressed as a function of frequency is the correct manner of expressing this physical characteristic since the pattern by which the wave is re–emitted in the medium is a function only of the frequency of disturbance induced by the incident radiation into the N dipole re–emitters and the spatial pattern of the re–emitters that is characteristic of the medium itself. The incident wavelength is *extinguished.* $n(\lambda)$ expressed as function of wavelength, often found throughout the establishment and at least implied if not applied in most text books, is an incorrect formulation, thus leading to incorrect conclusions and assumptions on convection of light.

In **Figures** 8 and 9, it is shown that in each case of refracting media, since the frequency of interference that excites the absorbing face of the medium must be equal to the frequency at the face that re–emits the secondary wave, the medium is always the equivalent of a window when applying the *extinction shift principle*. The *effective length* or window thickness is $L'(\nu)$, where $L'(\nu) \ / \ L = n(\nu)$, L being the actual physical length. The ***effective*** **velocity is** $U = c \ / \ n(\nu)$ in the medium, and thus the transit time over the length L is a function of $\nu = \nu_0(1 - \frac{v}{c})$ and thus an indirect function of the velocity v of the motion of the medium. **See Appendix IV: Moving/Fixed Windows Principal Axioms.**

All waves propagate with velocity c with respect to their most immediate *primary* sources, the N–ary re–emitters or dipole elements in the medium. [3]

Convection using Extinction Shift

Refracting Medium with Index of Refraction $n(\nu_0)$

NOTED BY *HYPOTHETICAL OBSERVER* { IN THE **MEDIUM** FRAME }

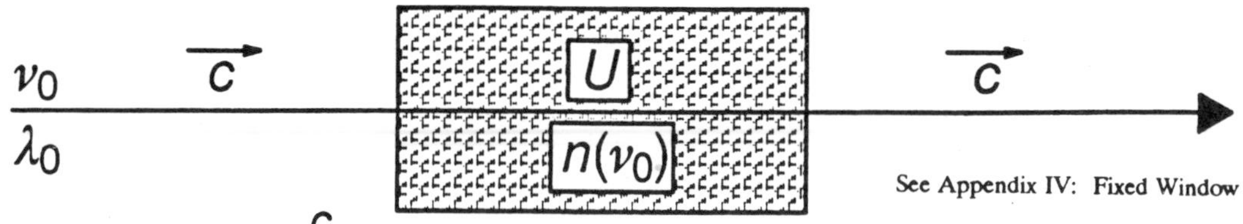

$$U = \frac{c}{n(\nu_0)}$$

Fixed medium

See Appendix IV: Fixed Window of Principal Axioms, page 20A.

Moving medium

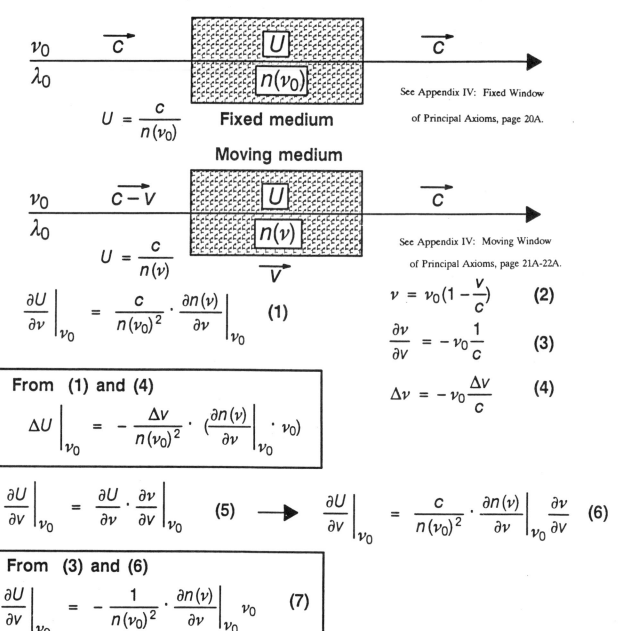

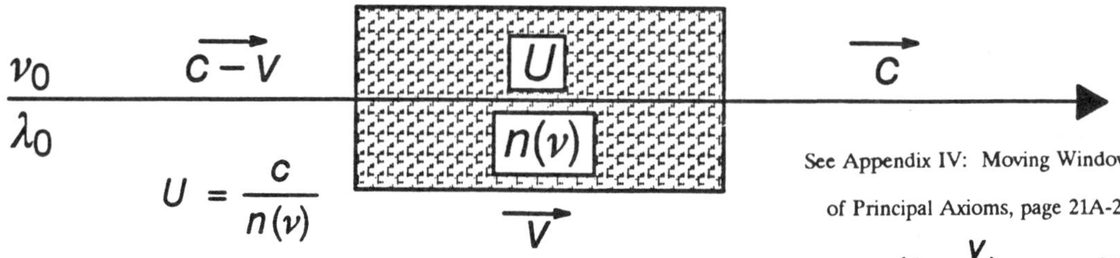

$$U = \frac{c}{n(\nu)}$$

See Appendix IV: Moving Window of Principal Axioms, page 21A-22A.

$$\left.\frac{\partial U}{\partial \nu}\right|_{\nu_0} = \frac{c}{n(\nu_0)^2} \cdot \left.\frac{\partial n(\nu)}{\partial \nu}\right|_{\nu_0} \qquad (1)$$

$$\nu = \nu_0\left(1 - \frac{V}{c}\right) \qquad (2)$$

$$\frac{\partial \nu}{\partial V} = -\nu_0 \frac{1}{c} \qquad (3)$$

$$\Delta \nu = -\nu_0 \frac{\Delta V}{c} \qquad (4)$$

From (1) and (4)

$$\left.\Delta U\right|_{\nu_0} = -\frac{\Delta V}{n(\nu_0)^2} \cdot \left(\left.\frac{\partial n(\nu)}{\partial \nu}\right|_{\nu_0} \cdot \nu_0\right)$$

$$\left.\frac{\partial U}{\partial V}\right|_{\nu_0} = \frac{\partial U}{\partial \nu} \cdot \left.\frac{\partial \nu}{\partial V}\right|_{\nu_0} \qquad (5) \longrightarrow \left.\frac{\partial U}{\partial V}\right|_{\nu_0} = \frac{c}{n(\nu_0)^2} \cdot \left.\frac{\partial n(\nu)}{\partial \nu}\right|_{\nu_0} \frac{\partial \nu}{\partial V} \qquad (6)$$

From (3) and (6)

$$\left.\frac{\partial U}{\partial V}\right|_{\nu_0} = -\frac{1}{n(\nu_0)^2} \cdot \left.\frac{\partial n(\nu)}{\partial \nu}\right|_{\nu_0} \nu_0 \qquad (7)$$

Note: constant c does not appear in (7).

Figure 8

Convection using Extinction Shift

Refracting Medium with Index of Refraction $n(\nu)$

NOTED BY *HYPOTHETICAL OBSERVER* { IN THE **REST** FRAME }

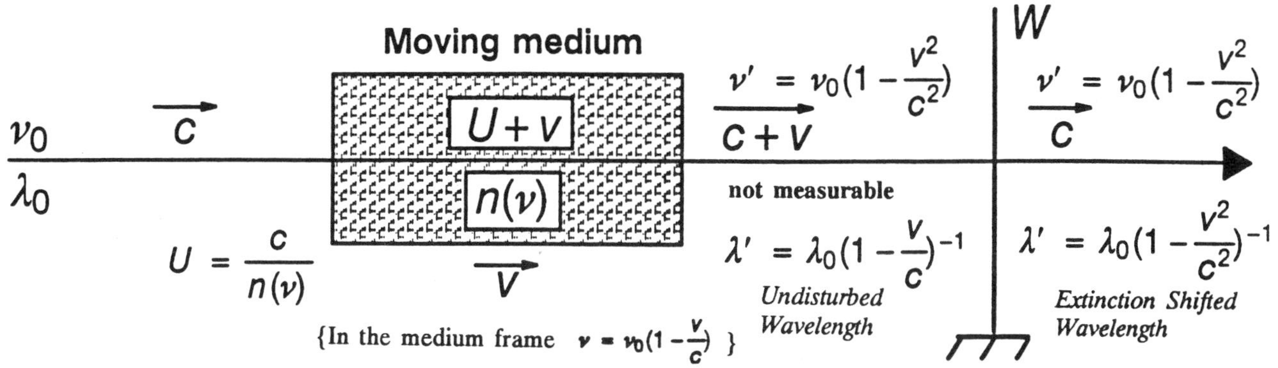

See Appendix IV: Moving Window of Principal Axioms, page 21A-22A.

$$\left.\frac{\partial U}{\partial v}\right|_{\nu_0} = -\frac{1}{n(\nu_0)^2} \cdot \left.\frac{\partial n(\nu)}{\partial \nu}\right|_{\nu_0} \nu_0 \qquad (7)$$

Let change in v $= \Delta v = \vec{V}$

$$\left. U + \Delta v + \Delta U \right|_{\nu_0} = U + \Delta v - \frac{1}{n(\nu_0)^2} \cdot \left.\frac{\partial n(\nu)}{\partial \nu}\right|_{\nu_0} \nu_0 \cdot \Delta v$$

$$\left. U + \Delta v + \Delta U \right|_{\nu_0} = U + \left(1 - \frac{1}{n(\nu_0)^2} \cdot \left.\frac{\partial n(\nu)}{\partial \nu}\right|_{\nu_0} \nu_0 \right) \Delta v$$

Note: constant c does not appear.

Figure 9

On the effective as opposed to actual mass change as function of velocity of mass

Extinction Shift Principle Illustrated; Some Classical Alternatives equivalent to Special and General Relativistic Principles

In Figures 10 and 11, using *extinction shift principle* and Galilean transformations to derive the effective path lengths as a result of changes in propagation time–of–flight, an alternative calculation for the relativistic effects can be obtained. In Figure 10, it is shown that an equivalent *effectivistic* or apparent mass as opposed to the *relativistic* mass can be derived without requiring any change in the *actual* mass as a function of velocity.[4]

Since the mass particle is in motion, the force field acting on it would have to propagate over an increased round-trip path, from the moving particle to the walls of the accelerator and then with *extinction shifted* velocity back to intercept the moving particle which will have moved to a new displaced position during the round-trip transit time of the field and its effects.

The field itself **does not** exert force on the mass particle. Force is transmitted via the field from the walls of the accelerator. The field is **massless!**

No length contraction or time dilation effects are assumed!

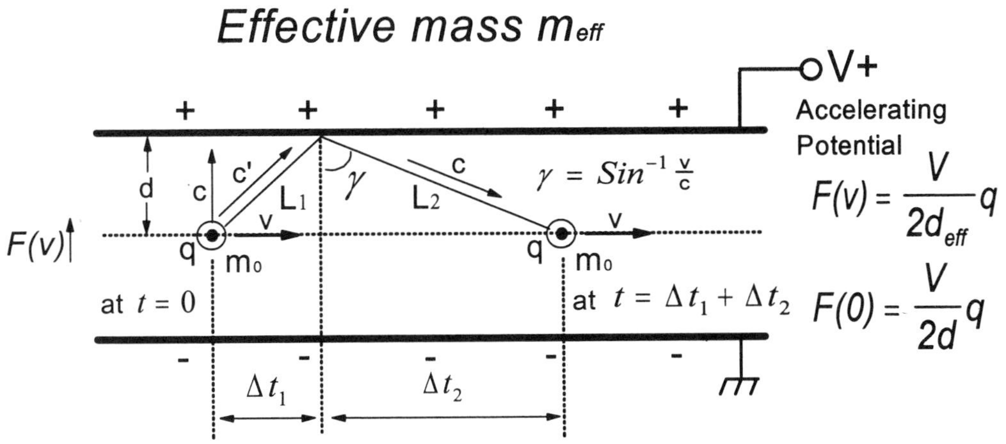

Figure 10

{Note: m_0 remains constant in Galilean Electrodynamics!}

$$c' = \sqrt{c^2 + v^2} \qquad Cos\gamma = \left(1 - \frac{v^2}{c^2}\right)^{-\frac{1}{2}}$$

$$\Delta t_1 = \frac{L_1}{c'} = \frac{d}{c} \qquad \Delta t_2 = \frac{L_2}{c} = \frac{d}{cCos\gamma} = \frac{d}{c}\left(1 - \frac{v^2}{c^2}\right)^{-\frac{1}{2}}$$

$$L_1 = \frac{c'}{c}d = d\left(1 + \frac{v^2}{c^2}\right)^{\frac{1}{2}} \qquad L_2 = d\left(1 - \frac{v^2}{c^2}\right)^{-\frac{1}{2}}$$

$$L_1 = d\left(1 + \frac{1}{2}\frac{v^2}{c^2} - \frac{1}{8}\frac{v^4}{c^4} + \ldots\right) \qquad L_2 = d\left(1 + \frac{1}{2}\frac{v^2}{c^2} + \frac{3}{8}\frac{v^4}{c^4} + \ldots\right)$$

The path ratio is $\frac{2d_{eff}}{2d} = \frac{L_1+L_2}{2d} = (1 + \frac{1}{2}\frac{v^2}{c^2} + \frac{1}{8}\frac{v^4}{c^4} + \ldots) \approx (1 - \frac{v^2}{c^2})^{-\frac{1}{2}}$ and the total transit time is $t = \Delta t_1 + \Delta t_2 = \frac{d}{c}[1 + (1 - \frac{v^2}{c^2})^{-\frac{1}{2}}] \approx \frac{d}{c}[(1 - \frac{v^2}{c^2})^{-\frac{1}{2}}]$. Thus, the *effective* distance is $d_{eff} = \frac{d}{\sqrt{1 - \frac{v^2}{c^2}}}$ from which a velocity dependent *effective* force of $F(v) = Eq = \frac{V}{2d_{eff}}q$ is gotten. An acceleration of $a = \frac{F}{m} = \frac{V}{2d_{eff}}q\frac{1}{m_0} = \frac{V}{2d}q\frac{1}{m_{eff}}$ results from which an *effective* {**not** the actual} mass of $m_{eff} = \frac{m_0}{\sqrt{1 - \frac{v^2}{c^2}}}$ is gotten from the *Extinction Shift Principle*. An effective mass change may be given as $\Delta m = m_{eff} - m_0 = m_0(1 - \frac{v^2}{c^2})^{-\frac{1}{2}} - m_0$. Equating energy and *effective* mass, a maximum value of $\Delta m = m_0$ may be given by $m_0(1 + \frac{1}{2}\frac{v^2}{c^2}) - m_0 = \{\frac{1}{2}m_0 v^2\}\frac{1}{c^2} = E\frac{1}{c^2}$.

Thus, the energy required for this *effective* mass change is therefore $E = \Delta mc^2 = m_0c^2$.

Extinction Shift Principle Illustrated; Some Classical Alternatives equivalent to Special and General Relativity Principles

On *Transverse Relative Time* $\tau' = \dfrac{\tau_0}{\sqrt{1-\frac{v^2}{c^2}}}$ under Electrodynamics of *Extinction Shift Principle* as opposed to *Time Dilation*

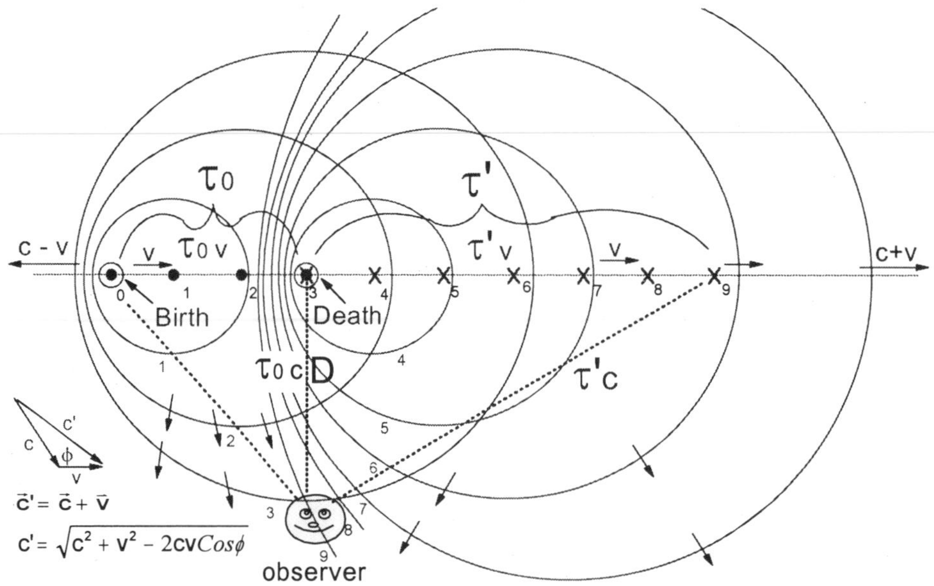

Figure 10B

Let a source move with constant velocity V in a direction transversely relative to a stationary observer as indicated in Figure 10B. Assume the source has a lifetime of τ_0 seconds and emits two bursts of signals, an initial one at birth ($t = 0$) and a final one at death ($t = 3$). The resting observer is placed at a distance D from the nearest point on the path of the moving source. Let the initial burst serve as time reference and be emitted such that it is received at the observer's measuring apparatus when the source is positioned such that a line extended from the observer to the source is at right angle to the path of the source (dotted line). It is herewith mathematically illustrated that the difference in the times of arrival of the initial and final waves is actually $\tau' > \tau_0$; a *transverse relative time* shift, the inverse of a *transverse relative frequency* shift. As a consequence of Galilean transformations and the rectilinear path of all constituent parts of a wave front, *a simultaneous detection by a single observer of both the initial and the final signal busts is not possible!* The initial wave front will arrive at the speed $c' = \sqrt{c^2 + v^2}$ for the distance $\sqrt{D^2 + D^2 \frac{v^2}{c^2}}$ and have the radius $D = \tau_0 c$. The final wave is emitted at distance $\tau_0 V$ past the point of emission of the initial wave. The final wave front is received at the observer delayed by τ' seconds, during which time the center of the spherical wave front moves the distance $\tau' v$ past the $t = 3$ point to the $t = 9$ point, while its radius increases to the length of $\tau' c$. It follows from geometry that $(\tau' c)^2 = (\tau_0 c)^2 + (\tau' v)^2$. Solving for τ' we get $\tau' = \dfrac{\tau_0}{\sqrt{1-\frac{v^2}{c^2}}}$. Thus, a particle of lifetime τ_0 and velocity v will appear to any fixed observer to move the distance $\tau' v$ in time $\tau' = \dfrac{\tau_0}{\sqrt{1-\frac{v^2}{c^2}}}$.

This effect is therefore a *transverse relative time shift*, **not** a time dilation!

On rectilinear path of gravitation of mass particles under one another's influence and effect on planetary motion as function of relative velocity of influenced mass particle and field set up by influencing mass

Extinction Shift Principle Illustrated; Some Classical Alternatives equivalent to Special and General Relativistic Principles

In **Figure** 11, it is shown that by using solely Galilean transformations, *effective* lengths and the *extinction shift principle*, the ***perihelion rotational effect*** of the planet Mercury can be calculated without employing *relativistic* assumptions. As in the case of the Sagnac effect previously illustrated, gravitation as well as all other radiation always **propagates *in a rectilinear fashion*.** The propagating gravitational field governing planetary motion *does not* rotate ! Thus, the force and effects are all functions of the relative motion of mass particles and the field set up by the other mass particles under its influence! The alternative result here is precisely the mathematical equivalence of the results obtained using relativistic assumptions. [4]

No mass change, length contraction or time dilation effects are assumed!

Perihelion Rotation of Mercury using *Extinction Shift Principle*

M and m remain constant in Galilean Electrodynamics!

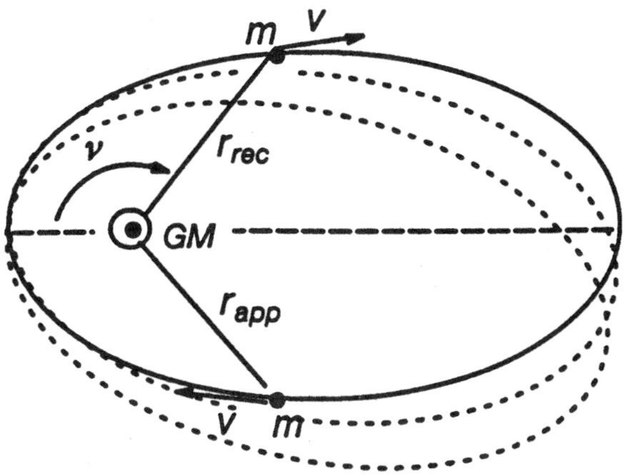

Figure 11 A

r_{rec} = **effective length { receding }**
r_{app} = **effective length { approaching }**

Effective force is $F_{rec} = \frac{GMm}{r^2_{rec}}, \quad F_{app} = \frac{GMm}{r^2_{app}}$

$$GM = 1.3271544 \cdot 10^{20}\ m^3/s^2$$
$$a = 57.9 \cdot 10^9\ m$$
$$e = 0.205633$$
$$r = a(\ 1-e^2\ )/((1+eCos\nu)$$
$$\omega = \sqrt{\frac{GM}{r^3}} \qquad v = \sqrt{\frac{GM}{r}}$$
$$\frac{v^2}{c^2} \approx 2.663 \cdot 10^{-8}$$

Assume that any force or perturbational effect transmitted via gravity will propagate with velocity c relative to its primary point of origin, m or M. Consequently, along the return path, completing the reflected energy exchange information on m and using the Galilean transformation, the return effect will propagate with velocity $c' = \sqrt{c^2 \pm v^2 \mp 2vcCos\phi}$ { an *Extinction Shifted* gravitational reflection from m back to M }.
v is the velocity of the orbital motion of m at the angle ϕ relative to the direction of propagation of the field G with velocity c relative to M. { The resultant velocity c' has practically the same angle ϕ relative to v since $\frac{v}{c} \ll 1$ in a Kepler orbit, sweeping the same angular history for ϕ, for $0 < \nu < \pi$ and $\pi < \nu < 2\pi$ }. [4]

Perihelion Rotation of Mercury using *Extinction Shift Principle*

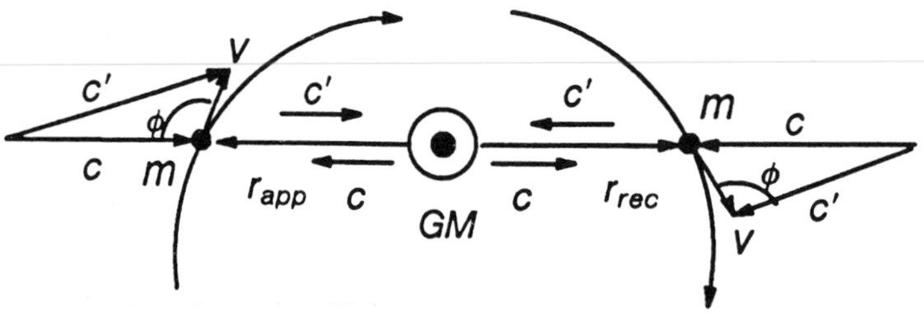

Figure 11 B

Effective length calculation as function of $\frac{v}{c}$:

For receding m : $0 < \nu < \pi$

$$c' = \sqrt{c^2 - v^2 + 2vc'Cos\phi}$$

$$2vc'Cos\phi \approx 2vcCos\phi$$

$$c' = c(1 - \frac{v^2}{c^2} + 2\frac{v}{c}Cos\phi)^{\frac{1}{2}}$$

$$\tau_{rec} = \frac{r}{c'}\ , \qquad r = \frac{a(\ 1 - e^2\ )}{1 + eCos\nu}$$

$$r_{rec} = c\tau_{rec} = r(1 - \frac{v^2}{c^2} + 2\frac{v}{c}Cos\phi)^{-\frac{1}{2}}$$

$$r_{rec} \approx r(1 + \frac{1}{2}\frac{v^2}{c^2} - \frac{v}{c}Cos\phi)$$

For approaching m : $\pi < \nu < 2\pi$

$$c' = \sqrt{c^2 + v^2 - 2vcCos\phi}$$

$$c' = c(1 + \frac{v^2}{c^2} - 2\frac{v}{c}Cos\phi)^{\frac{1}{2}}$$

$$\tau_{app} = \frac{r}{c'}$$

$$r_{app} = c\tau_{app} = r(1 + \frac{v^2}{c^2} - 2\frac{v}{c}Cos\phi)^{-\frac{1}{2}}$$

$$r_{app} \approx r(1 - \frac{1}{2}\frac{v^2}{c^2} + \frac{v}{c}Cos\phi)$$

$$\omega_{rec} = \sqrt{\frac{GM}{r_{rec}^3}} = \sqrt{\frac{GM}{r^3}}[1 - \frac{v^2}{c^2} + 2\frac{v}{c}Cos\phi]^{\frac{3}{4}}$$

$$\omega_{app} = \sqrt{\frac{GM}{r_{app}^3}} = \sqrt{\frac{GM}{r^3}}[1 + \frac{v^2}{c^2} - 2\frac{v}{c}Cos\phi]^{\frac{3}{4}}$$

$$\omega_{rec} \approx \sqrt{\frac{GM}{r^3}}[1 - \frac{3}{4}\frac{v^2}{c^2} + \frac{3}{2}\frac{v}{c}Cos\phi] \quad \text{since } \frac{v}{c} \ll 1$$

$$\frac{d}{dv}\omega_{rec} = \sqrt{\frac{GM}{r^3}}[-\frac{3}{2}\frac{v}{c^2} + \frac{3}{2c}Cos\phi] \qquad \omega = \sqrt{\frac{GM}{r^3}}$$

$$\Delta\omega_{rec} = \omega\ (-\frac{3}{2}\frac{v}{c^2} + \frac{3}{2c}Cos\phi)\ \Delta v$$

$$\underset{\Delta v = +v}{\Delta\omega_{rec}} = \omega\ (-\frac{3}{2}\frac{(+v)^2}{c^2} + \frac{3}{2}\frac{(+v)}{c}Cos\phi)$$

similarly

$$\underset{\Delta v = -v}{\Delta\omega_{app}} = \omega\ (+\frac{3}{2}\frac{(-v)^2}{c^2} - \frac{3}{2}\frac{(-v)}{c}Cos\phi)$$

Net change in angular rate $\Delta\omega = \Delta\omega_{rec} - \Delta\omega_{app}$

Note: odd terms $\{\ \frac{3v}{2c}Cos\phi\ \}$ **cancel**

$$\Delta\omega = \omega\ [(-\frac{3v^2}{2c^2}) - (+\frac{3v^2}{2c^2})]$$

$$\Delta\omega = \omega \cdot 3\frac{v^2}{c^2} = \frac{3\omega\ GM}{a(1 - e^2)c^2} \qquad \nu = \frac{\pi}{2}$$

$$\Delta\omega = 7.04814 \cdot 10^{-14}\ rad/sec$$

$$\Delta\omega\frac{2\pi}{\omega} = \frac{6\pi\ GM}{a(1 - e^2)}\frac{1}{c^2} = 5.019568 \cdot 10^{-7}\ rad/period = 42.988\ arcsec/century$$

Perihelion Rotation of PSR 1913 + 16 Binary Pulsar using *Extinction Shift Principle*

M_p and M_c remain constant in Galilean Electrodynamics!

A radio binary pulsar system PSR 1913 + 16, discovered in 1977, consisting of two masses M_p and M_c orbiting about their center–of–mass point, as illustrated in Figure 12A, is currently being claimed by relativists as a modern test confirming General Relativity.[5] However, it is shown here that by using solely Galilean transformations along with the concept of *extinction shifting* of the gravitational effects, the results obtained are mathematically equivalent to the results using procedures of General Relativity. The observed effects noted in the binary pulsar system are calculated using the concept of *extinction shifting* of the perturbational effects of the two mass bodies under one another's influence. The effects transmitted via primary gravitational waves propagate with velocity c relative to the perturbing mass, but with velocity c′ relative to the perturbed mass. This procedure is found to be equivalent to that of General Relativity.[4]

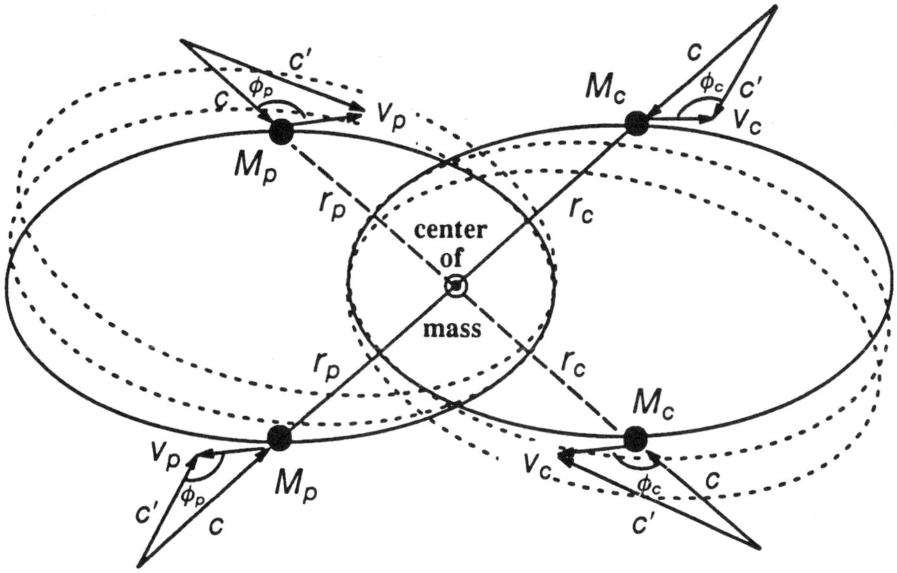

$M_p : M_c$ Center–of–mass system

Figure 12A

Extinction Shift Principle Illustrated; Some Classical Alternatives equivalent to Special and General Relativistic Principles

Observed over a period of years since 1977, the orbital period of the PSR1913 + 16 pulsar system is precisely determined, thus permitting additional parameters characterizing the system to be derived or calculated as summarized in the box below:

$G = 6.672 \cdot 10^{-11}\ m^3/s^2$	$\tau_p = 27906.98\ seconds$
$GM\Theta = 1.3271544 \cdot 10^{20}\ m^3/s^2$	$= 7.7519394\ hours$
$M_p = 1.439\ M\Theta$	$\omega_p = 2.2514745 \cdot 10^{-4}\ rad/sec$
$M_c = 1.389\ M\Theta$	$e = 0.617155$
$r_p = 9.917533429 \cdot 10^8 m$	$r_c = 9.572935324 \cdot 10^8 m$

Assume that any perturbational effect transmitted via gravity propagates with velocity c relative to its primary source mass M_p or M_c. Consequently, along the return path, the reflected energy exchange information on the perturbing mass, using the Galilean transformation, will propagate with velocity $c' = \sqrt{c^2 \pm v^2 \mp 2vcCos\phi}$ {an *Extinction Shifted* gravitational reflection from M_p to M_c and reciprocally, from M_c back to M_p}. v_p and v_c are the respective velocities as seen from the center–of–mass reference frame (Figure 12A). $v = v_p - v_c$ is the velocity of orbital motion of M_p and M_c relative to one another's frame of reference.

Moving about the center–of–mass point, M_p has the velocity $c_p' = \sqrt{c^2 \pm v_p^2 \mp 2v_pcCos\phi_p}$ relative to the gravitational field set up by M_c. Vice versa, M_c has the velocity $c_c' = \sqrt{c^2 \pm v_c^2 \mp 2v_ccCos\phi_c}$ relative to the field set up by M_p. ϕ_p and ϕ_c are the angles between the direction of motion of the respective masses and the direction of propagation of the gravitational field set up by the other mass. The resultant velocities c_p' and c_c' are pointing practically in the same direction as the propagation velocity of the gravitational field since $\frac{v}{c} \ll 1$ and in a Kepler orbit, the angles ϕ_p and ϕ_c are swept through practically the same angular history for $0 < \nu < \pi$ and $\pi < \nu < 2\pi$.

Under Galilean transformation, where the propagation velocity c of the gravitational field is additive to the velocity v of the mass that sets up the field, it does not matter whether the reference frame chosen is that of the center–of–mass of M_p and M_c, as illustrated in Figure 12A, or the reference frame of either M_p or M_c, as illustrated in Figure 12B. The problem is analytically the equivalent of M_p orbiting about M_c with velocity $v = v_p - v_c$, which is the relative velocity of M_p and M_c. In the M_c Reference–frame system (Figure 12B), the velocity of M_p is $c' = \sqrt{c^2 \pm v^2 \mp 2vcCos\phi}$ relative to the field set up by M_c where ϕ is the angle between the direction of motion of M_p and the direction of propagation of the field set up by M_c. Since $\frac{v}{c} \ll 1$ then the velocity vectors c' and c are pointing practically in the same direction.

Assume that gravitational waves propagate as any electromagnetic radiation, and that the Galilean transformation holds. The effective distance $r_{effective}$ and, therefore, the force transmitted by gravity are functions of the velocity of relative motion between the two masses M_p and M_c (under one another's influence).

The effective path length $r_{effective}$ in a Kepler orbit can be expressed essentially as the gravitational transit time from a moving mass $\tau_{eff} = \frac{r}{c'}$ times the propagation velocity of gravity from a stationary mass $\{ r_{eff} = c\tau_{eff} \}$.
For approaching and receding cases, $r_{app} = [\frac{c}{c'}r]_{app}$ and $r_{rec} = [\frac{c}{c'}r]_{rec}$ are denoted as the corresponding effective lengths depicted in Figure 12B .

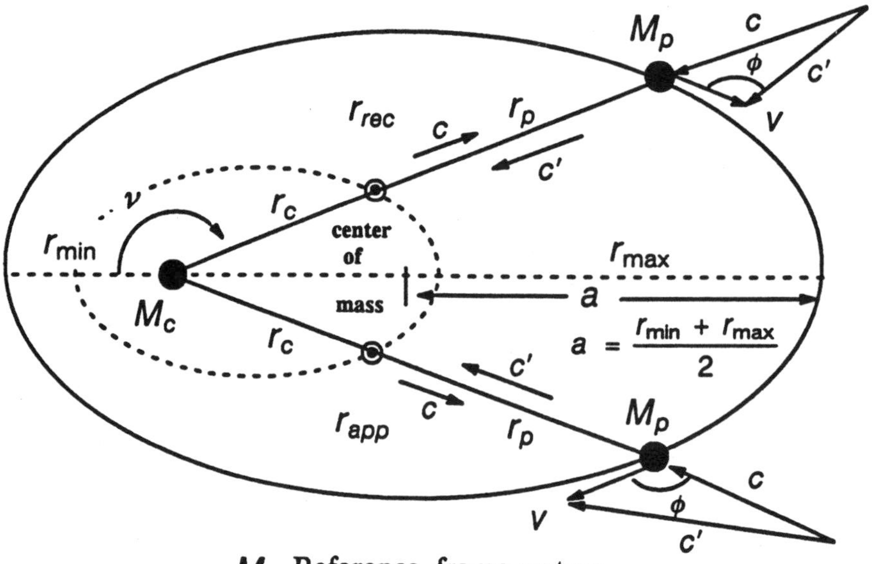

M_c Reference–frame system

Figure 12B

$r_{rec} = (r_p + r_c)_{rec}$ = **effective distance** $\{ M_p$ *to* M_c **receding** $\}$
$r_{app} = (r_p + r_c)_{app}$ = **effective distance** $\{ M_p$ *to* M_c **approaching** $\}$

Effective force is $F_{rec} = \frac{G(M_p M_c)}{r^2_{rec}}$ and $F_{app} = \frac{G(M_p M_c)}{r^2_{app}}$

where $r = r_p + r_c = \sqrt[3]{\frac{G(M_p + M_c)}{\omega^2}}$

In the M_c reference–frame system, Figure 12B, the indicated velocities and vectors are given as viewed from M_c . The ellipse described by the motion of M_p is the composite of the two ellipses in Figure 12A. The center-of-mass point describes also an ellipse { dotted line ellipse } with identical eccentricity $e = 0.617155$.

As a result, the lengths describing the orbit are as follows:

$$r(\omega) = r_p + r_c = \sqrt[3]{\frac{G(M_p + M_c)}{\omega^2}}$$

$$r_{min} = (r_p + r_c)(\ 1 - e\ ) \qquad r_{min} = r(\ 1 - e\ ) \qquad where\ 2a = r_{min} + r_{max}$$

$$r_{max} = (r_p + r_c)(\ 1 + e\ ) \qquad r_{max} = r(\ 1 + e\ ) \qquad a = \frac{r_{min} + r_{max}}{2}$$

$$r = r_p + r_c \qquad M = M_p + M_c$$

$$r_{rec} = (r_p + r_c)_{rec}$$

$$\omega = \sqrt{\frac{G(M_p + M_c)}{(r_p + r_c)^3}} = \sqrt{\frac{GM}{r^3}}$$

$$r_{app} = (r_p + r_c)_{app}$$

Using the Galilean transformation, the effective lengths for both the approaching and receding portions, $0 < \nu < \pi$ and $\pi < \nu < 2\pi$ of the elliptical orbit of M_p is derived as follows:

Effective length calculation as function of $\frac{v}{c}$ for receding M_p { $0 < \nu < \pi$ }:

$$c' = \sqrt{c^2 - v^2 + 2vc'Cos\phi}$$

$$2vc'Cos\phi \approx 2vcCos\phi$$

$$c' = c(1 - \frac{v^2}{c^2} + 2\frac{v}{c}Cos\phi)^{\frac{1}{2}}$$

$$\tau_{rec} = \frac{r}{c'}\ , \qquad r = \frac{a(\ 1 - e^2\ )}{1 + eCos\nu}$$

$$r_{rec} = c\tau_{rec} = r(1 - \frac{v^2}{c^2} + 2\frac{v}{c}Cos\phi)^{-\frac{1}{2}}$$

$$r_{rec} \approx r(1 + \frac{1}{2}\frac{v^2}{c^2} - \frac{v}{c}Cos\phi)$$

Extinction Shift Principle Illustrated; Some Classical Alternatives equivalent to Special and General Relativistic Principles

Effective length calculation as function of $\frac{v}{c}$ for approaching $M_p \{ \pi < \nu < 2\pi \}$

$$c' = \sqrt{c^2 + v^2 - 2vcCos\phi}$$

$$c' = c(1 + \frac{v^2}{c^2} - 2\frac{v}{c}Cos\phi)^{\frac{1}{2}}$$

$$\tau_{app} = \frac{r}{c'}$$

$$r_{app} = c\tau_{app} = r(1 + \frac{v^2}{c^2} - 2\frac{v}{c}Cos\phi)^{-\frac{1}{2}}$$

$$r_{app} \approx r(1 - \frac{1}{2}\frac{v^2}{c^2} + \frac{v}{c}Cos\phi)$$

Using the observed mean angular rate $\omega = 2.2514745 \cdot 10^{-4}$ *rad/sec* for the PSR 1913+16 binary pulsar system and the ordinary Kepler laws, the change in angular rate $\Delta\omega = 2.3374954 \cdot 10^{-9}$ *rad/sec* is found without Relativity as follows:

$$\omega_{rec} = \sqrt{\frac{GM}{r_{rec}^3}} = \sqrt{\frac{GM}{r^3}}[1 - \frac{v^2}{c^2} + 2\frac{v}{c}Cos\phi]^{\frac{3}{4}}$$

$$\omega_{app} = \sqrt{\frac{GM}{r_{app}^3}} = \sqrt{\frac{GM}{r^3}}[1 + \frac{v^2}{c^2} - 2\frac{v}{c}Cos\phi]^{\frac{3}{4}}$$

$$\omega_{rec} \approx \sqrt{\frac{GM}{r^3}}[1 - \frac{3}{4}\frac{v^2}{c^2} + \frac{3}{2}\frac{v}{c}Cos\phi] \quad \text{since } \frac{v}{c} \ll 1$$

$$\omega_{rec} \approx \omega\ [1 - \frac{3}{4}\frac{v^2}{c^2} + \frac{3}{2}\frac{v}{c}Cos\phi] \quad where\ \omega = \sqrt{\frac{GM}{r^3}}$$

$$\frac{d}{dv}\omega_{rec} = \omega\ [-\frac{3}{2}\frac{v}{c^2} + \frac{3}{2c}Cos\phi]$$

$$\Delta\omega_{rec} = \omega\ (-\frac{3}{2}\frac{v}{c^2} + \frac{3}{2c}Cos\phi)\ \Delta v$$

$$\Delta\omega_{rec} = \omega\ (-\frac{3}{2}\frac{(+v)^2}{c^2} + \frac{3}{2}\frac{(+v)}{c}Cos\phi) \quad \Delta v = +v$$

similarly

$$\Delta\omega_{app} = \omega\ (+\frac{3}{2}\frac{(-v)^2}{c^2} - \frac{3}{2}\frac{(-v)}{c}Cos\phi) \quad \Delta v = -v$$

Net change in angular rate $\Delta\omega = \Delta\omega_{rec} - \Delta\omega_{app}$

Note: odd terms $\{ \frac{3v}{2c}Cos\phi \}$ **cancel**

$$\Delta\omega = \omega\ [(-\frac{3v^2}{2c^2}) - (+\frac{3v^2}{2c^2})]$$

$$\Delta\omega = \omega\ 3\frac{v^2}{c^2} = \frac{3\omega\ GM}{a(1-e^2)c^2} \qquad \nu = \frac{\pi}{2}$$

$$\Delta\omega = 2.3374954 \cdot 10^{-9}\ rad/sec$$

$$\Delta\omega = \frac{3\omega\ G(M_p + M_c)}{a(1-e^2)}\frac{1}{c^2} = 4.2265\ degrees\ per\ year$$

Conclusion

With proper applications of the *extinction shift principle* using solely Galilean transformations and elementary mathematics, alternative calculations for all physical effects previously requiring relativistic treatments can be accomplished. The *extinction shift principle* is consistent with the findings of all experiments in optics to first order in $\frac{v}{c}$ and correctly predicts the null results in all previous experimental efforts designed to test the constancy of the velocity of light theory. There are therefore no requirements necessary for length contractions, time dilations or relativistic masses.

The *true*, natural wavelength of *undisturbed* radiation does not depend on the reference frame. Thus, a wavelength of radiation cannot be *shifted* according to the established definition of the *Doppler principle,* but rather re–emitted as an *extinction shifted* secondary wave. Consequently, there is no physical requirement that the velocity of propagation of electromagnetic, electrostatic, magnetic or gravitational fields or their effects remain constant in all frames of reference. The propagation velocity of all fields and the effects thereof obey the Galilean transformation $c' = c + v$, whereby c' is the velocity of the *undisturbed* radiation, v is the velocity of its *most direct primary* source and c is the constant of the natural velocity of radiation relative to its *primary* source.

Laboratory and astronomical observations may be considered as direct evidence for the validity of the properly applied *extinction shift principle* with Galilean Electrodynamics, thus rendering the *Special* and *General Relativistic principles* as mere equivalences to natural laws.

Effectivity, an Alternative to Relativity

RELATIVITY	***EFFECTIVITY***
{ c = const in all frames }	{ c = const relative to source } { $c \pm v$ relative to observer }
Doppler shifted wavelength	**Extinction shifted wavelength** { *undisturbed* λ preserved in all frames }
Doppler shifted frequency	**Relative frequency**
Transverse Doppler shift	**Transverse Relative frequency**
LORENTZ TRANSFORMATION	***GALILEAN TRANSFORMATION***
Relativistic length	**Effectivistic length**
Relativistic mass	**Effectivistic mass**
Dilated time	**Relative time = 1 / (Relative frequency)**

GLOSSARY OF TERMS

Effectivity — An alternative equivalence to relativity which employs the *Extinction Shift principle* and Galilean Transformations.

Undisturbed — *Not yet* interfered with or propagating *free* of matter–wave interaction with velocity c relative to its *most direct* source.

Galilean Transformation — $c' = c \pm (v_1 - v_2)$ is the interference–free propagation velocity of the *undisturbed* wave.

Extinction Shifted Wavelength — Wavelength of a re–emitted secondary wave with wavelength $\lambda' = \lambda_0(1 + \frac{v_1 - v_2}{c})^{-1}$, where λ_0 is the *undisturbed* wavelength of the primary wave, $v_1 - v_2$ is the relative velocity of the source and observer. The secondary wave is re–emitted on the frequency of the incident primary wave. [3]

Relative Frequency — The frequency $\nu' = \nu_0(1 + \frac{v_1 - v_2}{c})$ perceived by the observer whose velocity is $v_1 - v_2$ relative to the source on frequency ν_0. [3]

Transverse Relative Frequency — The frequency $\nu' = \nu_0(1 - \frac{(v_1 - v_2)^2}{c^2})$ perceived by observer looking transversely at source.

Transverse Relative Time — $\tau' = \frac{1}{\nu}' = \tau_0(1 - \frac{v^2}{c^2})^{-\frac{1}{2}}$

Effectivistic Length — $l_{eff} = l_0(1 - \frac{v^2}{c^2})^{\frac{1}{2}}$

Effectivistic Mass — $m_{eff} = m_0(1 - \frac{v^2}{c^2})^{-\frac{1}{2}}$

References

1. Redondi, Pietro, *Galileo : Heretic (Galileo Eretico)*, Princeton University Press, Princeton, New Jersey (1987).

2. Jackson, J.D., *Classical Electrodynamics*, John Wiley & Sons, Inc., New York, 512 - 515 (1975).

3. Dowdye, E.H., *Extinction Shift; an Alternative to the Doppler Shift Theory*, (Copyrighted work to be published) (1983).

4. Dowdye, E.H., *Extinction Shift Principle Illustrated; Some Classical Alternatives Equivalent to Special and General Relativistic Principles*,
(Copyrighted work to be published) (1991).

5. Hulse, R.A. and Taylor, J.H., *Science* **250**, 770 (1990); Hulse, R.A. and Taylor, J.H., *Astrophys. J.* **195**, L51 (1975).

Appendix

Appendix I

Aberrational Effect using the *Extinction Shift Principle* and the Concept of the Rectilinear Motion of the Photon

Extinguished (Disturbed) Aberrational Effect

Let a point source S move with velocity v and produce spherical waves of photons which are immediately extinguished. The direction of propagation of photons in the wave front will be defined by the secondary source, i.e., the point of re-emission. Photons of the re-emitted wave front will propagate rectilinearly with the velocity c relative to the fixed extinguishing medium, in the direction away from their point of emission. The angle θ is that angle between the source direction of motion and the line joining the observer and the apparent position of the source S'. The observer would note that the actual source position S would always deviate from the apparent source position S' by the angle x_1. In the *extinguished* case, the centers of the expanding spherical wave fronts will always remain tied to the **fixed** disturbing medium, at the point where the moving source S emitted the burst of photons. This becomes the apparent position S' of the expanding wave front. The actual position of the source S is as illustrated geometrically in Figure 1A.

Using the law of cosine twice, solving for the *effective* velocity V_{eff} of the wave front moving towards the observer from the actual source position S, $V_{eff} = \sqrt{c^2 + v^2 - 2cv\text{Cos}\theta}$, and then once again solving for $\text{Cos}\, x_1$, yielding $\text{Cos}\, x_1 = \dfrac{c^2 + V^2_{eff} - v^2}{2cV_{eff}}$, the calculated angle x_1 is thus:

$$x_1 = \text{Cos}^{-1}\left[\frac{1 - \frac{v}{c}\text{Cos}\theta}{\sqrt{1 + \frac{v^2}{c^2} - \frac{2v}{c}\text{Cos}\theta}}\right]$$

x_1 is the angle of separation between S and S' at the site of the observer for the *extinguished* case or for the case of the *disturbed* wave fronts.

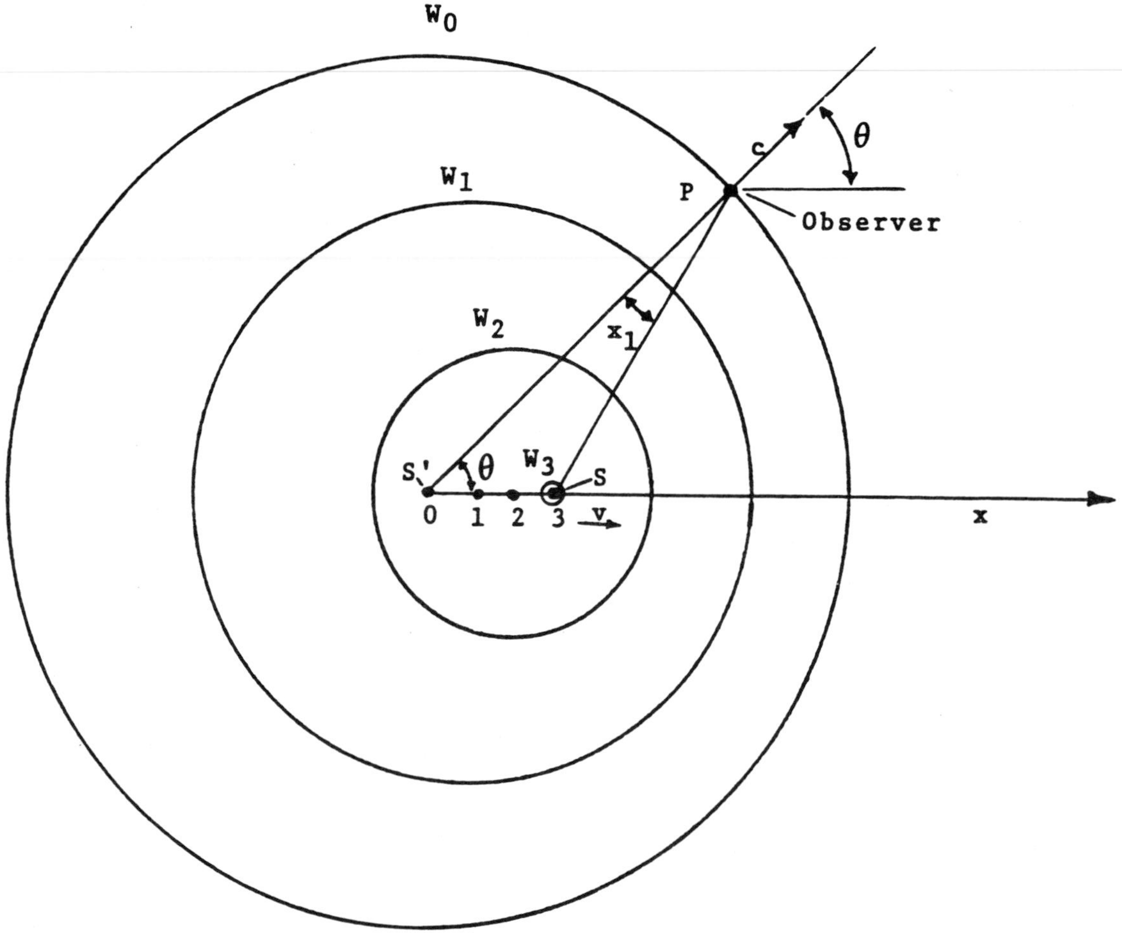

<u>Extinguished (Disturbed) Aberrational Effect</u>

Figure 1A

Appendix I

Aberrational Effect using the *Extinction Shift Principle* and the Concept of the Rectilinear Motion of the Photon

Extinction Free (Undisturbed) Aberrational Effect

Let a point source S move with velocity v and produce spherical waves of photons which are ***free*** of extinction. The direction of propagation of photons in the wave front will be defined by the vector sum of the source velocity V and the velocity c of the photons emitted by and relative to S, according to Galilean transformations. The angle θ is that angle between the source direction of motion and the line joining the observer and the apparent position of the source S'. The observer would note that the actual source position S would always deviate from the apparent source position S' by the angle x_2. In the *extinction free* case, the direction of propagation of constituent photons always points away from the actual source position S. The centers of the expanding spherical wave fronts will always coincide with the actual position of the source S as illustrated geometrically in Figure 2A.

Using the law of cosine twice, solving for the *effective* velocity V_{eff} of the wave front moving towards the observer from the actual source position S, $V_{eff} = \sqrt{c'^2 + v^2 - 2c'v\text{Cos}\theta}$, and then once again solving for $\text{Cos}\, x_2$, yielding $\text{Cos}\, x_2 = \dfrac{c'^2 + V^2_{eff} - v^2}{2c'V_{eff}}$, the calculated angle x_2 is thus:

$$x_2 = \text{Cos}^{-1}\left[\frac{1 - \frac{v}{c'}\text{Cos}\theta}{\sqrt{1 + \frac{v^2}{c'^2} - \frac{2v}{c'}\text{Cos}\theta}}\right]$$

where $c' = c + v$.

x_2 is the angle of separation between S and S' at the site of the observer for the *extinction free* case or for the case of the *undisturbed* wave fronts.

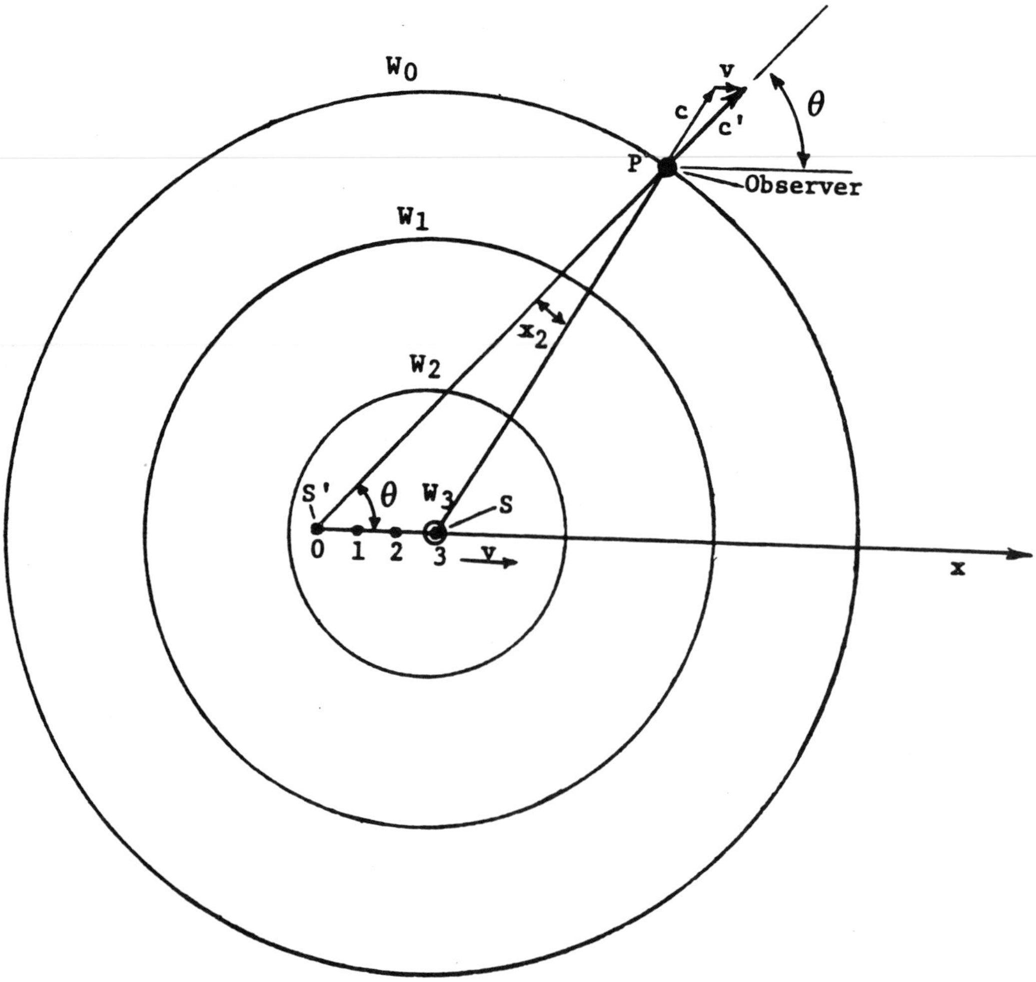

Extinction Free (Undisturbed) Aberrational Effect

Figure 2A

Appendix I

Aberrational Effect using the *Extinction Shift* Principle and the Concept of the Rectilinear Motion of the Photon

Distinguishability between the Extinguished and Extinction Free Aberrational Effects

The distinguishability between the *extinguished* and *extinction free* effects would require resolving the angles x_1 and x_2 where

$$x_1 = Cos^{-1}\left[\frac{1 - \frac{v}{c}Cos\theta}{\sqrt{1 + \frac{v^2}{c^2} - \frac{2v}{c}Cos\theta}}\right]$$

and

$$x_2 = Cos^{-1}\left[\frac{1 - \frac{v}{c'}Cos\theta}{\sqrt{1 + \frac{v^2}{c'^2} - \frac{2v}{c'}Cos\theta}}\right]$$

and where $c' = c + v$.

It is to be noted that at the most effective angle $\theta = 90^0$, the aberrational effect simplifies to $x_1 = Cos^{-1}(1 - \frac{1}{2}\frac{v^2}{c^2})$ and $x_2 = Cos^{-1}(1 - \frac{1}{2}\frac{v^2}{c'^2})$ to second order effect in $\frac{v}{c}$. Even at astronomical or fractional light velocities of v, an extinction of the primary wavefront would result in the re–emission and thus a new *disturbed* secondary wavefront, denying any measurement of x_2. Whether the photons are extinguished immediately at the point source or at a later time in the flight of the wavefront photons, the problem of re–emission of the wavefront is identical for the extinction of the point source and the extinction of the *extinction free* propagating spherical wavefront. Even without extinction, there is ***no*** current technical means of distinguishing between x_1 and x_2.

Appendix II

Proof of Galilean Transformation $c' = c + v$ using the *Extinction Shift* Principle, the Sagnac effect and the Concept of Rectilinear Motion of the Photon

The Sagnac effect may be graphically depicted as follows:

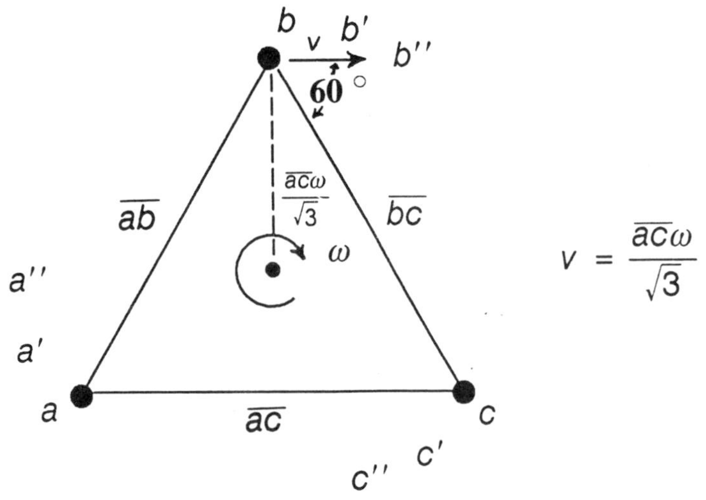

Point emitters of spherical waves rotate about a common center on a rigidly attached platform with angular rate ω **radians** per second. Photons **propagate** along a proper path from point a to the point b' ; i.e., the point where b will be positioned when the photons propagating rectilinearly intercept b at b'. The re–emitted photon of the same frequency, as seen in the frame of reference of the point b' , will propagate to point c'' , c'' to a''', etc., for the clockwise loop. For the counter–clockwise loop, the opposite sequence occurs; i.e., from a to c' , c' to b'', etc.

On basis of observational evidence, the concept of rectilinear path of the photon and the *extinction shift principle* as stated, the following may be given as proof of the Galilean transformation $c' = c + v$:

SAGNAC EFFECT "EXTINCTION SHIFT EXPLANATION"

Proof of Galilean Transformation

a) Let three or more points a , b and c be rigidly attached to a platform that rotates with constant angular rate ω relative to an inertial frame. Assume each point to be point sources of spherical waves.

b) Let point a emit a burst of photons at time t_o in all directions. Then any photon vectored in the direction of any of the lines joining the point a to the other points b and c at the instant in time t_o **when the** burst was released will not arrive at b or c since radiation propagates in a rectilinear path. **The** points constantly change their coordinates, and thus the required vector for photon hits at b or c .

c) The proper vector for photon hits are in the direction of the line $\overline{ab'}$ joining a and b' and the line $\overline{ac'}$ joining a and c' . **The** points b' and c' are the coordinates where the points b and c will be when the photons arrive at time $t_o + \overline{ab'}/c$ and $t_o + \overline{ac'}/c$ respectively, **and** where c is the propagation velocity of the photon relative to its most immediate source.

d) Thus, paths $\overline{ab}$ and $\overline{ac}$ require modification to paths $\overline{ab'}$ and $\overline{ac'}$. Similarly, the paths $\overline{ba}$ and $\overline{bc}$ require modification to $\overline{ba'}$ and $\overline{bc'}$. This holds in any rotating frame, thus changing the round–trip time of a signal and thus the relative phase for the two possible loops abc and cba .

e) Given that paths $\overline{ab} \neq \overline{ab'}$, $\overline{ac} \neq \overline{ac'}$ and $\overline{bc} \neq \overline{bc'}$ and also that paths $\overline{ab} = \overline{a'b'}$, $\overline{ac} = \overline{a'c'}$ and $\overline{bc} = \overline{b'c'}$ it follows that the above proves the equation $c' = c + v$ where v is the component of the velocity of motion of the point sources in the direction of the proper vector due to rotation at angular rate ω .

Proof of Galilean Transformation $c' = c + v$ **(Continued)**

f) From geometry, assuming equal path length $\overline{ab} = \overline{bc} = \overline{ca}$, the unmodified loop path of the photon is $\overline{ab} + \overline{bc} + \overline{ca} = 3\overline{ac}$, 3 times the width of the base of the triangle abc. If the angular velocity is about a common center, the velocity of the points is $\frac{\overline{ac}}{\sqrt{3}}\omega$ in a direction of 60^0 relative to the line joining a and c . The area enclosed by a, b and c is $A = \frac{\overline{ac}^2\sqrt{3}}{4}$. Thus, each point moves the distance $\frac{\overline{ac}}{\sqrt{3}}\omega \times \frac{\overline{ac'}}{c}$ during which time the photon propagates the distance $\overline{ac'}$ in $\frac{\overline{ac'}}{c}$ seconds. Since $\overline{ac} \approx \overline{ac'}$, the points move the distance $\frac{\omega\overline{ac}^2}{c\sqrt{3}} = aa' = b'b'' = c''c'''$ during the transit time $\frac{\overline{ac'}}{c}$ seconds. The path length will change by $\frac{\omega\overline{ac}^2}{c\sqrt{3}} \operatorname{Cos} 60^0$ in units of $\overline{ac}$.

g) The point a will have moved to a' , b to b' and c to c' during the transit time $\frac{\overline{ab'}}{c}$, $\frac{\overline{b'c''}}{c}$ or $\frac{\overline{c''a'''}}{c}$, etc, a change in the total path length of $(aa' + b'b'' + c''c''') \operatorname{Cos} 60^0$ which is $\frac{3\omega\overline{ac}^2}{c\sqrt{3}} \operatorname{Cos} 60^0$. Given that $A = \frac{\overline{ac}^2\sqrt{3}}{4}$, the change in the total loop path for one direction is $\Delta L = \frac{1}{2}\frac{4A}{c}\omega$. The net change in total loop path for clockwise and counter–clockwise directions is $\Delta L = \frac{4A}{c}\omega$. The total phase shift is $\Delta\phi = \frac{\Delta L}{\lambda} = \frac{4A}{\lambda c}\omega$, which is experimentally verified.

h) Since a , b and c have no relative motion with one another, it follows that there is no relative frequency shift. With the modified path length of $(aa' + b'b'' + c''c''') \operatorname{Cos} 60^0$ and the fact that the emitter and the secondary source both move with the same velocity component of $\frac{\overline{ac}}{\sqrt{3}}\omega \operatorname{Cos} 60^0$ in the same direction, it follows that with experimental validity of $\Delta\phi$, then $c' = c + v$ must be valid.

Appendix III

Gravitational Redshift: Using Moving Window Axiom of the *Extinction Shift* Principle

Let material particles of interstellar space be randomly distributed with random velocities and directions of motion. The particles of mass m have the kinetic energy of $\frac{1}{2} m\, v^2$. Assume this energy is comprised of the local temperature $T\ (k^o)$ and the gravitational potential energy $\{\ \phi\ \}$ of the surrounding interstellar space at the location of the re–emitting particles; i.e., the moving windows of interstellar space that are the secondary sources of cosmic photons. Given the thermal and kinetic energy relation $\frac{1}{2} m_i\, v_i^2 = \frac{3}{2} kT_i$, adding to this the energy contributed to the i–th particle by a gravitational force of potential ϕ_i given by $\int_R^\infty \frac{GMm_i}{R^2} dR = -\frac{GMm_i}{R} = \phi_i m_i$, then the total energy of the particle is given by $\frac{1}{2} m_i\, v_i^2 = \frac{3}{2} kT_i + \phi_i m_i$ where m_i is the mass of the i–th particle of temperature T_i , the local temperature and ϕ_i is the local gravitational gradient potential in that region of space. M is the mass of the source of the gravitational potential of radius R .

The particle of mass m_i is the secondary source positioned along the path of the primary photon, re–emitting it with velocity $c + v_i$. $\bar{x}$ is the mean–free–path of non–interference; i.e., the mean distance between the moving windows or secondary sources. Using the moving window axiom of the *extinction shift* principle, [9] the following illustration for the moving windows W_1 and W_2 applies:

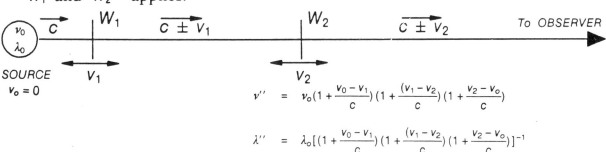

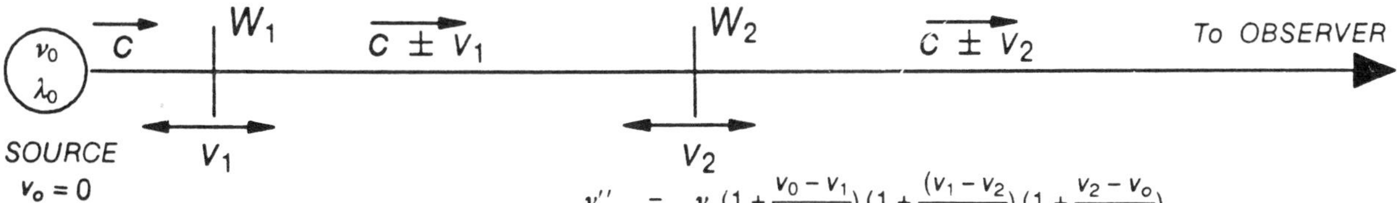

$$\nu'' = \nu_0 \left(1 + \frac{v_0 - v_1}{c}\right)\left(1 + \frac{(v_1 - v_2)}{c}\right)\left(1 + \frac{v_2 - v_o}{c}\right)$$

$$\lambda'' = \lambda_0 \left[\left(1 + \frac{v_0 - v_1}{c}\right)\left(1 + \frac{(v_1 - v_2)}{c}\right)\left(1 + \frac{v_2 - v_o}{c}\right)\right]^{-1}$$

Gravitational Redshift: Using Moving Window Axiom of the *Extinction Shift* Principle (Continued)

The moving window principle states that the shift in frequency is independent of the direction of motion of the window. This shift depends only on the velocity of the window and also on the number of windows { the number of re–emission events }. The shift is always one towards the red; i.e., a down shift in frequency and an increase in wavelength. An increase in the number of interferers with random directions of motion causes an accumulative effect. **It** reddens the frequency and increases the wavelength.

Analogous to moving windows are moving particles that cause re–emission of the primary photons along the path from the source of emission to the observer. If the sources of emission are stellar objects, the moving windows are moving material particles of interstellar space, the cosmic molecular gasses and dust clouds randomly distributed with random velocities and directions of motion. The moving window effect depends only on the component of the velocities of secondary sources pointing either in the same direction or against the direction of the photon propagation. Thus, all gravitational potentials along the path of the photon causing re–emitters to move non-perpendicularly to the direction of photon propagation contribute to the redshift.

This effect may be illustrated as follows:

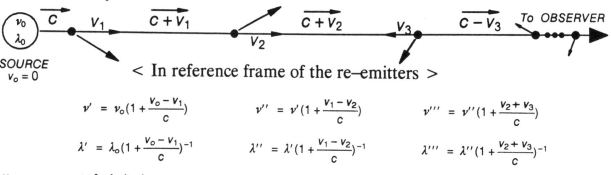

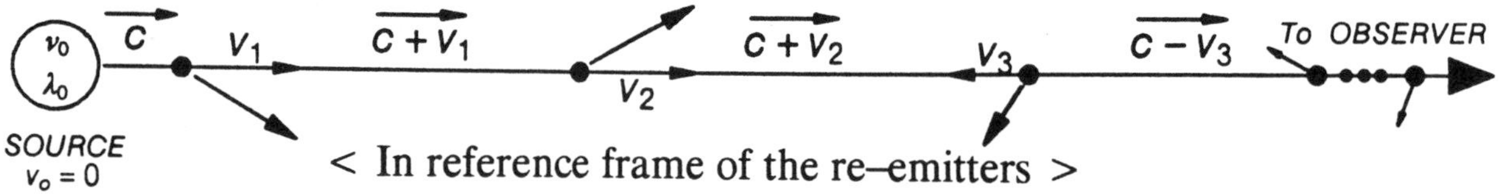

< In reference frame of the re–emitters >

$$\nu' = \nu_o\left(1 + \frac{V_o - V_1}{c}\right) \qquad \nu'' = \nu'\left(1 + \frac{V_1 - V_2}{c}\right) \qquad \nu''' = \nu''\left(1 + \frac{V_2 + V_3}{c}\right)$$

$$\lambda' = \lambda_o\left(1 + \frac{V_o - V_1}{c}\right)^{-1} \qquad \lambda'' = \lambda'\left(1 + \frac{V_1 - V_2}{c}\right)^{-1} \qquad \lambda''' = \lambda''\left(1 + \frac{V_2 + V_3}{c}\right)^{-1}$$

V_i = component of velocity due to local temperature and gravitational potential

● = moving re–emitter

Thus, to a fixed observer where $V_o = 0$ for the source and observer, the accumulative effect of the above illustrated frequency is

$$\nu'' = \nu_o\left(1 + \frac{V_o - V_1}{c}\right)\left(1 + \frac{(V_1 - V_2}{c}\right)\left(1 + \frac{V_2 + V_3}{c}\right)\left(1 + \frac{V_3 - V_o}{c}\right)$$

and the accumulative wavelength is

$$\lambda'' = \lambda_o\left[\left(1 + \frac{V_o - V_1}{c}\right)\left(1 + \frac{(V_1 - V_2}{c}\right)\left(1 + \frac{V_2 + V_3}{c}\right)\left(1 + \frac{V_3 - V_o}{c}\right)\right]^{-1} .$$

Gravitational Redshift: Using Moving Window Axiom of the *Extinction Shift* Principle (Continued)

The photon passing through interstellar space accumulates a reddening effect as it is re–emitted from the secondary source to the N–ary source according to $\nu^{(N)} = \nu_0 \prod_{i=1}^{N} (1 + \frac{v_{i-1} - v_i}{c})$. Assume $v_o = 0$ for a fixed primary source. An accumulative effect towards the red will always occur due to the temperature or to the random motion of the re–emitting secondary sources. Assuming that the gravitational potential energy is predominant, neglecting the temperature contribution, the square of the maximum velocity of free–fall of the i–th particle participating in the re–emission is $v_i^2 = 2\phi = \frac{2GM}{R}$. Any effect of the random relative velocities $v_{i-1} - v_i$ of adjacent re–emitters due to temperature would be negligible in comparison to that of the predominant gravitational potential energy since any medium participating in the re–emission process, exposed to the same predominating gravitational potential will move practically in the same direction with similar velocities. Hence, $| v_{i-1} - v_i | \ll | v_i - v_o |$; $v_o = 0$

and $\nu^{(N)} \approx \nu_0 (1 + \frac{v_0 - v_i}{c})(1 + \frac{(v_i - v_0)}{c}) = \nu_0 (1 - \frac{v_i^2}{c^2})$.

As a consequence of the moving window axiom, a group of windows moving with the same velocity is the optical equivalence of a single moving window with that velocity. Thus, for a group of re–emitters in a volume exposed to the same gravitational potential, the extinction length $\bar{x}$ will not be an important factor and the maximum redshift along a line joining the source of the gravitational potential and the observer is then given by $\Delta\nu = \nu_0 \frac{2GM}{Rc^2}$.

This is however the maximum effect along the photon path for the maximum velocity of free–fall of moving secondary sources pointing directly towards or away from the observer. Integrating over a sphere around the source of the gravitational potential, the effective volume of influence, i.e., the mean effect of moving emitters due to the potential around the gravitating mass pointing in the direction of the observer for a unit sphere, **is given by the integral of** the volume element of the sphere times $\sin\phi \sin\theta$ divided by the total volume of the sphere of re–emitters.

Gravitational Redshift: Using Moving Window Axiom of the *Extinction Shift* Principle (Continued)

For secondary photons coming from the hemisphere facing the observer, the effective volume of influence for a mean redshift is:

$$\bar{V} = \frac{\int_{r=0}^{r=1} r^2 dr \int_{\phi=0}^{\phi=\pi} Sin^2\phi \, d\phi \int_{\theta=0}^{\theta=\pi} Sin\theta \, d\theta}{\int_{r=0}^{r=1} r^2 dr \int_{\phi=0}^{\phi=\pi} Sin\phi \, d\phi \int_{\theta=0}^{\theta=\pi} d\theta} = \frac{\frac{\pi}{3}}{\frac{2\pi}{3}} = \frac{1}{2}$$

Thus, from the ***extinction shift principle*** using the moving window axiom, a mean gravitational redshift is then $\Delta\nu = \frac{1}{2} \nu_o \frac{2GM}{Rc^2} = \nu_o \frac{GM}{Rc^2}$, which is well within the current technical means of astronomical observation and is due to the photons re–emitted from the moving cosmological windows of secondary sources.

A *gravitational* blue-shift of photons caused by moving re-emitters, according to the *extinction shift principle*, cannot take place. Moreover, there is not a shred of observational evidence for a *gravitational* blue-shift!

Important Note: A *gravitational* redshift, as defined by the *extinction shift principle*, has **no** dependency at all on the relative motion of the primary source and the receiver! This shift is always one towards the red (See Moving Window Axiom of the *Extinction Shift Principle*, p. 21A). The redshift is actually caused by material secondary sources of emission of interstellar space. The *secondary* sources *extinguish* and then re-emit the *primary* photons from a frame of reference other than that of the *primary* source and of the receiver. The motion of the re-emitting *secondary* source media; i.e., the dipole re-emitters contained in the dark-matter of interstellar space, is governed primarily by the predominant gravitational field.

Gravitational Redshift: Light Bending using Moving Window Axiom of the *Extinction Shift* Principle
Solar Light Bending

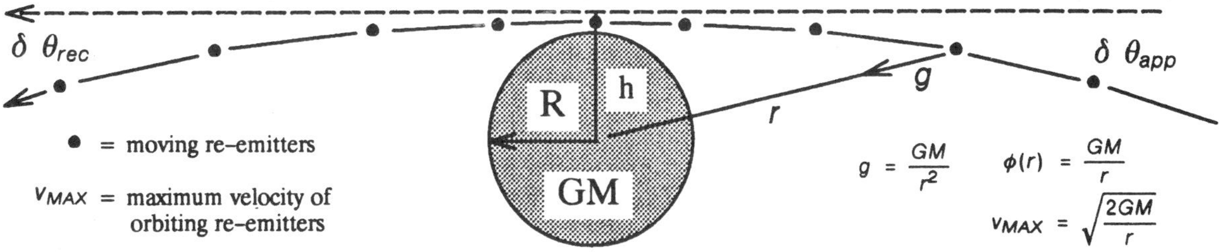

Let material particles of the solar corona have random velocities such that their kinetic energies are as dictated by $\frac{1}{2}m\ v^2 = \frac{3}{2}kT + \phi m$ where m is the mean mass of the particles of the corona, $T\ (\ k^o\ )$ is the temperature and v is the velocity of the plasma particles bounded by the total energy of the gravitational potential given by $\phi\ \binom{r=\infty}{r=R} = \int_{\infty}^{R} \frac{GM}{r^2} dr = \frac{GM}{R}$ as illustrated above. At the temperature and density of the corona region, an extremely high vacuum, the occurrence of particle velocities exceeding $v = \sqrt{2\phi} = \sqrt{\frac{2GM}{R}}$ may be considered unlikely and thus contributing negligibly to the effect as the rate of loss of solar mass is negligible.

Thus, the velocity $v = \sqrt{\frac{2GM}{R}}$; i.e., the escape velocity at $h = R$ may be assigned as an upper bound for the velocity of moving secondary emitters in the solar corona region. From the moving window axiom, the frequency and wavelength from moving secondary sources at velocity v are:

$$\nu' = \nu_o(1 - \frac{v^2}{c^2}) = \nu_o(1 - \frac{2GM}{Rc^2})$$

$$\lambda' = \lambda_o(1 - \frac{v^2}{c^2})^{-1} = \lambda_o(1 - \frac{2GM}{Rc^2})^{-1} \approx \lambda_o(1 + \frac{2GM}{Rc^2})$$

Note that here again the maximum velocity of the moving re–emitters is a function of the maximum energy of the gravitational potential $\phi\ \binom{r=\infty}{r=R} = \frac{GM}{R}$. The extinction length parameter $\bar{x}$ for the solar corona region is unknown and may be considered on the order of the mean–free–path of the re–emitters at corona vacuum { very long }. The resulting shift from the moving window axiom is *not* dependent on the *direction* of motion but rather *is* dependent on the *magnitude* of the velocity component along the path of the photon!

Gravitational Redshift: Solar Light Bending (Continued)

Extinction Shift Principle

According to the moving window axiom of the *extinction shift* principle, [9] the maximum shift in the wavelength of photons re–emitted by secondary sources at any radial distance r is $\Delta\lambda = \lambda' - \lambda_o$ where $\lambda' = \lambda_o(1 - \frac{2GM}{rc^2})^{-1}$. Thus, the number of wavelengths along the path of the photons per unit length may be given as

$$n = \frac{1}{\lambda'} = \frac{1}{\lambda_o(1 - \frac{2GM}{rc^2})^{-1}} = \frac{1}{\lambda_o}(1 - \frac{2GM}{rc^2}) \quad .$$

Thus, the energy ϵ per unit length along the photon path is $\epsilon = \epsilon_o(1 - \frac{2GM}{rc^2})$. Consequently, the number of re–emitted waves per unit length along the photon path and thus the energy per unit length increases as r increases. This translates to a downward, *re–emitted path* of the photon, in straight line segments of **rectilinear** paths between re–emitters, along a minimum energy path on approach of the photon.

If $\frac{d\epsilon}{dr} = +\epsilon_o\frac{2GM}{r^2c^2}$ or $\Delta\epsilon = +\epsilon_o\frac{2GM}{r^2c^2}\Delta R$, then the re–emission of photons will occur on a path such that the total energy along the path would not change. If ϵ is the energy per unit length along the photon path and $\Delta\epsilon$ is the change in energy in the direction of the gradient potential $\phi(r)$, then the angle of path change during approach is

$$\delta\theta_{app} = \frac{\Delta\epsilon_{app}}{\epsilon} = +\int_{r=\infty}^{r=R} \frac{2GM}{r^2c^2}dr = -\frac{2GM}{Rc^2}$$

and the path change during receding is

$$\delta\theta_{rec} = \frac{\Delta\epsilon_{rec}}{\epsilon} = +\int_{r=R}^{r=\infty} \frac{2GM}{r^2c^2}dr = +\frac{2GM}{Rc^2} \quad .$$

The net path change is

$$\delta\theta = \delta\theta_{rec} - \delta\theta_{app} = \frac{4GM}{Rc^2} \quad .$$

Gravitational Redshift: Solar Light Bending (Continued)
Extinction Shift Principle

Note: The change in photon path as predicted by the *extinction shift* principle is due solely to re–emission by the moving windows or secondary sources whose velocity is bounded by the total energy of the solar gravitational potential $\phi \left({}^{r=\infty}_{r=R} \right)$.

The photon path is always one of a rectilinear path between processes of emission and is neither **accelerating nor orbiting** on a curved path about the gravitating mass. As in Galilean Electrodynamics, the photon is **massless**!

Appendix IV

Extinction Shift Principle applied to *Nullified Experiments in Optics*

Null results in experiments designed to test the constancy of the velocity of light may be explainable with a hypothesized re–emission concept whereby an undisturbed incident light propagates with predetermined velocity and wavelength *(unmeasurable)* quantities until it is absorbed and re–emitted with new *extinction shifted* velocity and wavelength *(measurable)* quantities. The relative frequency of the moving source is passed (remains unchanged) during the re–emission process into the frame of reference of the interference. Thus, as a consequence of *extinction,* as will be illustrated later, a fringe shift pattern registered as a function of the velocity of moving source, does not occur.

Consider a fixed source that turns on for a time duration of τ seconds, producing a light pulse whose length is $L = \tau c$. If all references were made with respect to the rest frame, a moving light source with the same time duration would emit a light pulse that would extend the distance $(c+v)\tau$ while the source moves the distance $v\tau$ before turning off. A fixed hypothetical observer { $v_0 = 0$ } capable of observing this light pulse without disturbing it would note that the light pulse would have the length $(c+v)\tau - v\tau = c\tau$. This is the same pulse length produced by the fixed light source. The hypothetical observer would also note that the undisturbed, faster light pulse would fly by a fixed point with velocity $c+v$ in the time $\tau' = L/(c+v) = \tau(1+\frac{v}{c})^{-1}$. If this pulse were disturbed by some fixed point of interference (*measured with ordinary means*), the resulting re–emitted, secondary light pulse would have the same time duration τ' as the faster, primary light pulse, but would be re–emitted with a shorter, *extinction shifted* length $L' = L(1+\frac{v}{c})^{-1}$ and with velocity c relative to the point of interference.

Extinction Shift Principle applied to *Nullified Experiments in Optics*

Analogous to the disturbed light pulse of length $L' = L(1+\frac{v}{c})^{-1}$ and the time duration $\tau' = \tau(1+\frac{v}{c})^{-1}$ for the re–emitted pulse, a measurement would yield in every case only the *extinction shifted* wavelength $\lambda' = \lambda_0(1+\frac{v}{c})^{-1}$ and relative frequency $\nu' = \nu_0(1+\frac{v}{c})$ of light emitted from a source approaching with velocity v. Thus, a wavelength of primary light cannot be Doppler shifted but rather re–emitted as an *extinction shifted* secondary light wave with the relative frequency of the source, as would be noted in the frame of reference of the interference.

In the illustrations to follow, the moving and fixed elements involving a source, mirror(s) and/or window(s) are denoted by the symbols S, M and W, respectively. The motion and direction of the elements are indicated by the symbols ←, → or ↔ and the fixed elements by  .

In this paper, we shall assume the hypothetical case of an ideal vacuum, and that the Galilean transformation $c' = c + v$ holds. Thus, no length contractions or time dilations can be realized. Any process of re–emission will extinguish the incident *primary* light, replacing it with *secondary* light that propagates with velocity c, with respect to its new *secondary* source, the mirror or the window. Assume also that the motion in each case is along a linear path, in the indicated direction with constant velocity v for all moving elements and that the observer throughout the paper is the *hypothetical* observer, moving with velocity v_0 and is capable of observing all events without interfering.

Extinction Shift **Principle applied to** *Nullified Experiments in Optics*

Extinction Shift Theory Illustrated

PRINCIPAL AXIOMS

The *extinction shift* is illustrated on various optical paths, some of which are equivalent to some well known experiments on the constancy of the velocity of light. These experiments may involve any one of the following cases:

1. Moving light source with fixed mirror(s) and/or window(s)
2. Moving window(s) with fixed light source
3. Moving mirror(s) with fixed light source
4. Moving window(s) with fixed light source, window(s) and/or mirror(s)
5. Moving mirror(s) with fixed light source, window(s) and/or mirror(s)

Examples of optical experiments are illustrated where in each case, the hypothetical observer notes the undisturbed output frequency and wavelength of the primary light as a function of the velocities of the moving element(s). It is to be assumed that the rays of light are, in each case, incident perpendicularly at the surfaces of the mirrors and windows.

In Figure 1, a hypothetical observer of velocity $v_0 = 0$ reads the output of the experiment and notes the undisturbed light pulse of intensity I, created by the source S of velocity $v_1 = v$ and time constant τ for the time duration $\tau' = \tau(1 + \frac{v_1 - v_0}{c})^{-1} = \tau(1 + \frac{v}{c})^{-1}$, the undisturbed pulse length L and the propagation velocity $c + v_1 - v_0 = c + v$.

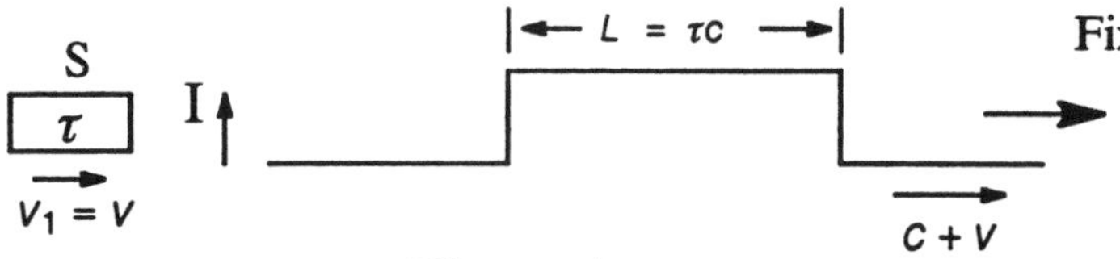

Fixed Hypothetical Observer $v_0 = 0$

$\tau' = L/(c+v) = \tau(1 + \frac{v}{c})^{-1}$
and
$L' = L$

Figure 1

Extinction Shift Theory Illustrated (Continued)

PRINCIPAL AXIOMS

In Figure 2 an undisturbed primary light pulse of length L is incident at a fixed window W of velocity $v_2 = 0$ with velocity $c + v_1 - v_2 = c + v$. It is absorbed and propagated in the window medium with velocity c/n which is characteristic of the properties of the window medium with index of refraction n . The pulse is re-emitted with velocity $c + v_2 = c$ relative to the rest frame by W , a secondary source moving with velocity $v_2 = 0$. In the re-emission process, from primary to secondary wave, the velocity of propagation is reduced by the factor $\frac{c}{c+v} = (1 + \frac{v}{c})^{-1}$ for an approaching source. It is logical to assume that the time duration by which the window face is illuminated by the incident primary light pulse with velocity $c + v$ would be equal to the time duration of the secondary pulse, re-emitted from the window with velocity c . Thus, the relative time duration τ' will not change for the light pulse during the re-emission process and the *extinction shift will result in a decreased/increased length of the re-emitted pulse by the factor* $(1 \pm \frac{v}{c})^{-1}$ *for an approaching/receding light source of velocity* $\pm v$. Hence, only the *extinction shifted* pulse length $L(1 + \frac{v}{c})^{-1}$ of an undisturbed pulse of length L would be measurable from a source of time constant τ , approaching with velocity v as illustrated in Figure 2.

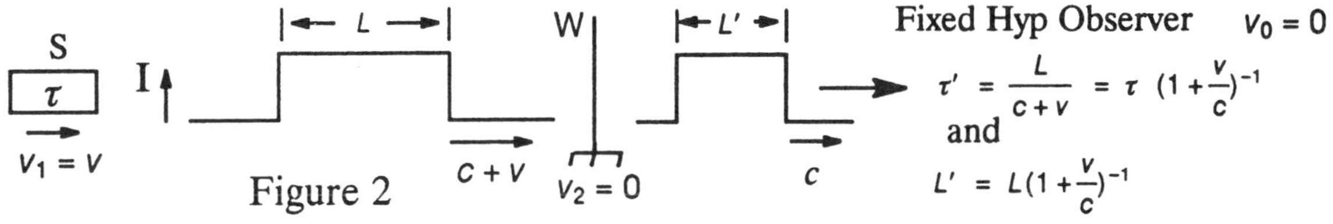

Figure 2

The invariance of τ' during the re-emission process of the light pulse implies that the relative frequency ν' of any wave, when disturbed by a fixed point of interference, namely by a fixed window or mirror, would not change. This is therefore consistent with the logical assumption that the number of primary waves absorbed at the face of a fixed window per unit time is equal to the number of waves transmitted in the window medium and then re-emitted at the other face per unit time.

Extinction Shift Theory Illustrated (Continued)

PRINCIPAL AXIOMS

Consequently, an *extinction shift of velocity and wavelength caused by a fixed disturber would not alter the relative frequency of the incident primary wave*. The fixed hypothetical observer, would therefore note that *the frequency of the re–emitted, extinction shifted wave would always equal the relative frequency of the incident, undisturbed primary wave*.

In Figure 3, the hypothetical observer of velocity v_0 would note here that the undisturbed wavelength λ_0 of the *extinction–free propagating primary wave* is independent of both the source velocity v_1 and the observer's velocity v_0 and that the relative frequency ν' and the propagation velocity $c + v_1 - v_0 = c \pm v$ of the primary wave are functions of the relative velocity $v_1 - v_0$ of the source and the observer.

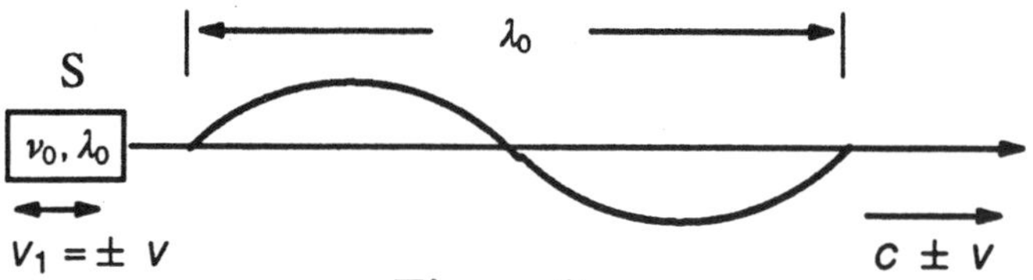

Figure 3

Hyp Observer with velocity v_0

$$\nu' = \nu_0\left(1 + \frac{\pm v - v_0}{c}\right)$$

$$\lambda' = \lambda_0$$

Fixed Hyp Observer $v_0 = 0$

$$\nu' = \nu_0\left(1 \pm \frac{v}{c}\right)$$

$$\lambda' = \lambda_0$$

Any measurement by ordinary means would cause the velocity and wavelength of the primary wave at the output in Figure 3 to be re–emitted , as illustrated in Figure 4 , by the secondary source, the fixed window W ($v_2 = 0$).

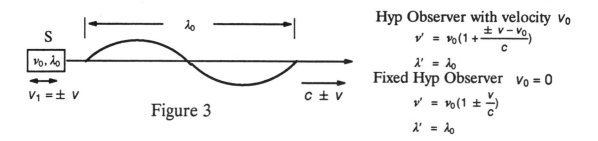

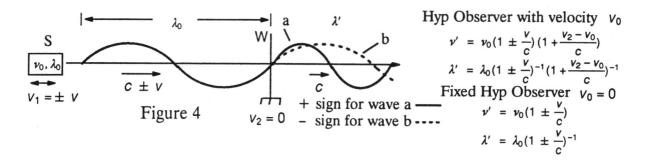

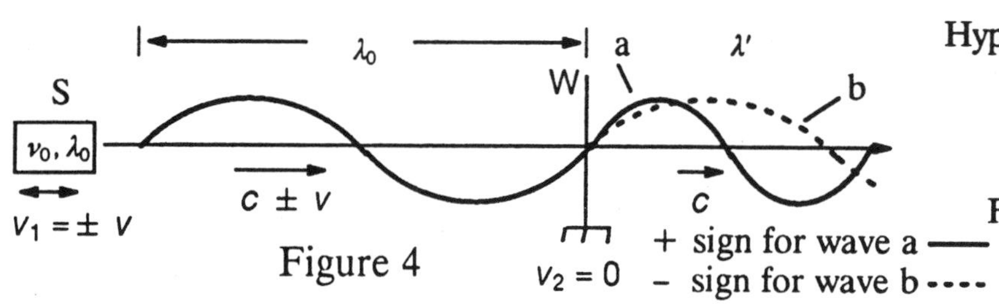

Figure 4

Hyp Observer with velocity v_0

$$\nu' = \nu_0\left(1 \pm \frac{v}{c}\right)\left(1 + \frac{v_2 - v_0}{c}\right)$$

$$\lambda' = \lambda_0\left(1 \pm \frac{v}{c}\right)^{-1}\left(1 + \frac{v_2 - v_0}{c}\right)^{-1}$$

Fixed Hyp Observer $v_0 = 0$

$$\nu' = \nu_0\left(1 \pm \frac{v}{c}\right)$$

$$\lambda' = \lambda_0\left(1 \pm \frac{v}{c}\right)^{-1}$$

Extinction Shift Theory Illustrated (Continued)

PRINCIPAL AXIOMS

Analogous to the pulse length illustrated in Figure 2, the observer in Figure 4 notes a primary–to–secondary shift in the propagation velocity and wavelength of the wave by the factor $\frac{c}{c \pm v}$ for an approaching/receding source of velocity $\pm v$. He also notes that the relative frequency ν' of the primary light is not altered during the process of re–emission of the primary light into secondary light by the fixed window.

A mirror reflection of a primary–to–secondary light wave, as illustrated in Figure 5, is optically equivalent to a window transmission illustrated in Figure 4, as would be perceived by an observer in the same reference frame as that of the window or mirror $\{ v_1 - v_0 = 0 \}$.

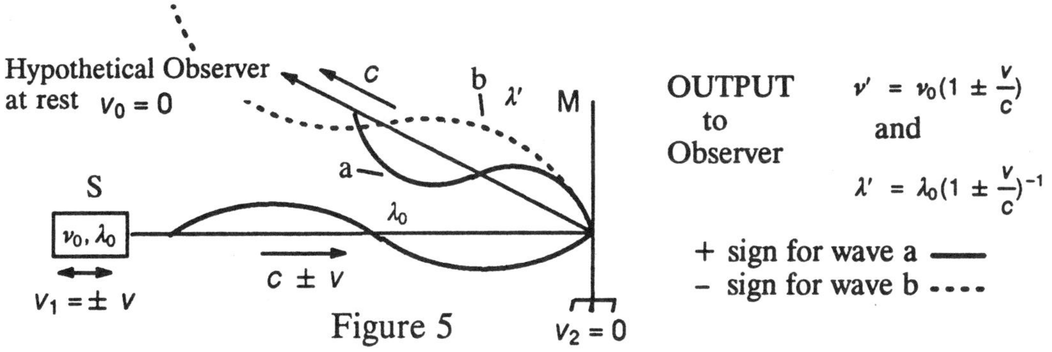

Figure 5

In Figure 6, the window W_1 recedes/approaches a fixed source S and is illuminated at the relative frequency $\nu_0(1 \mp \frac{v}{c})$ by the source on frequency ν_0. W_1 window then re–emits another wave on that frequency as would be noted by an observer in that frame of reference. W_2 then re–emits a wave on the relative frequency of W_1 as perceived in the frame of reference of W_2.

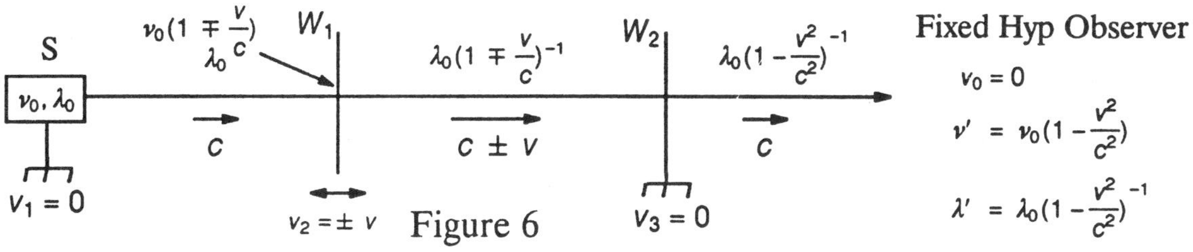

Figure 6

Extinction Shift Principle applied to *Nullified Experiments in Optics*

Extinction Shift Theory Illustrated (Continued)

PRINCIPAL AXIOMS

Note: The wavelength and frequency at the output of W_2 noted in Figure 6 is independent of the direction of motion of the moving window W_1 .

Note: A group of N windows moving with the same velocity and direction, not separated by a fixed window or fixed interference of velocity $v_0 = 0$ { *undisturbed* waves between windows }, is the optical equivalence of a single moving window. N windows moving with the velocity of W_1 , either approaching or receding the observer, separated by fixed interference or fixed windows, would serve only to increase the effect of the single moving window noted in Figure 6 by a factor of N . Hence, the accumulative frequency and wavelength is

$$\nu^{(N)} = \nu_o(1+\frac{v_0-v_1}{c})(1+\frac{v_1-v_0}{c})(1+\frac{v_0-v_2}{c})(1+\frac{v_2-v_0}{c})\cdots(1+\frac{v_N-v_0}{c})(1+\frac{v_0-v_N}{c}) \approx \nu_o(1-N\frac{v^2}{c^2})$$

$$\lambda^{(N)} = \lambda_o[(1+\frac{v_0-v_1}{c})(1+\frac{v_1-v_0}{c})(1+\frac{v_0-v_2}{c})(1+\frac{v_2-v_0}{c})\cdots(1+\frac{v_N-v_0}{c})(1+\frac{v_0-v_N}{c})]^{-1} \approx \lambda_o(1-N\frac{v^2}{c^2})^{-1} .$$

In Figure 7, the mirror approaches / recedes the fixed observer. In the mirror's frame of reference, the relative frequency $\nu_0(1 \pm \frac{v}{c})$ is noted. In the fixed frame, the frequency $\nu_0(1 \pm \frac{v}{c})^2$ is noted. The fixed hypothetical observer notes the velocity $c \pm v$ and the wavelength $\lambda_0(1 \pm \frac{v}{c})^{-1}$, which are again not measurable.

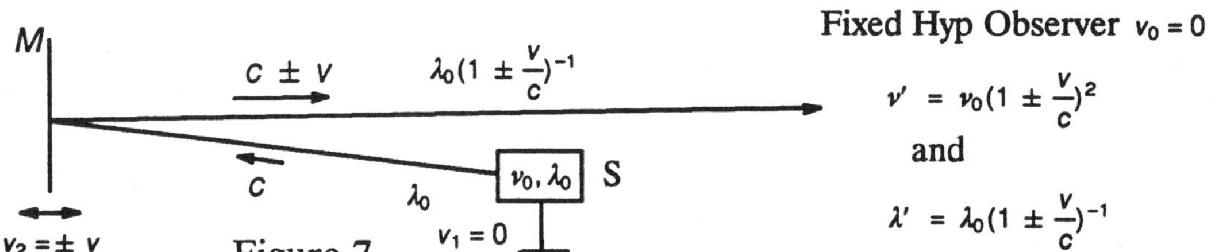

Figure 7

A measurement on the output in Figure 7 would yield the *extinction shifted* wavelength $\lambda_0(1 \pm \frac{v}{c})^{-2}$ and the relative frequency $\nu_0(1 \pm \frac{v}{c})^2$, passed by any window in the observers frame of reference.

Extinction Shift Theory Applied to Nullified Experiments

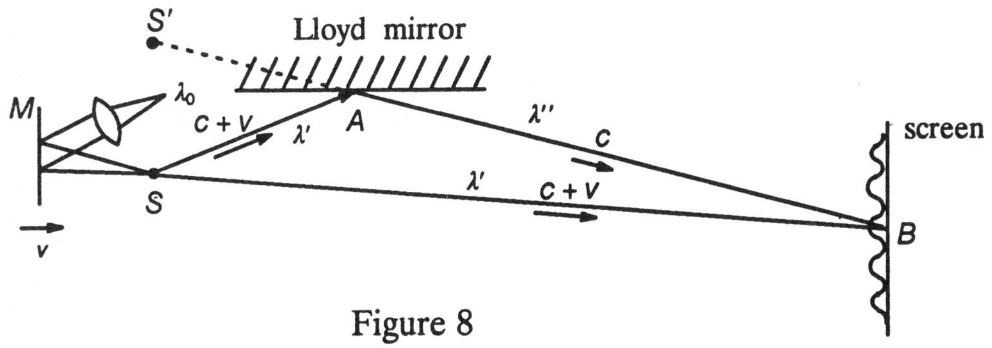

Figure 8

In Figure 8, a moving mirror was employed in the experiment performed by P. Beckmann and P. Mandics [3] in an attempt to test the constancy of the velocity of light. We shall assume that in this experiment an ideal vacuum was at hand. The light with path SA and SB in Figure 8 actually propagated with velocity $c+v$ and that the process of extinction occurred as hypothesized resulting in the light of path AB with velocity c .

Interference fringes are formed by the images of the light source S and S', S' being the image of S through the Lloyd mirror. Using the postulates derived and illustrated above, we find that the light with path SA and SB , propagating with velocity $c+v$, has the wavelength $\lambda' = \lambda_0(1+\frac{v}{c})^{-1}$, where λ_0 is the *undisturbed* wavelength of the primary wave reflected by M. The light ray with path SA gives rise to the ray AB with velocity c and wavelength $\lambda'' = \lambda'(1+\frac{v}{c})^{-1} = \lambda_0(1+\frac{v}{c})^{-2}$, caused by the Lloyd mirror reflection, the equivalent of the postulated effect illustrated in Figure 7.

Extinction Shift Theory Applied to Nullified Experiments (Continued)

The light with paths AB, SA and SB all have the same frequency since the Lloyd mirror is a stationary interferer. Therefore, the relative phase of the interfering light at B is a function only of the wavelengths and velocities of the light rays SB and AB. We may write

$$\Phi = \Phi(\lambda_0, v) \qquad \text{and} \qquad \Delta\Phi = \frac{d}{dv}\Phi(\lambda_0, v)$$

where Φ is the relative phase of the interfering light at B and $\Delta\Phi$ is the change in the relative phase of the light rays SB and AB as a function of the velocity v of the moving source. We may split this function into two separate parts to represent the relative phase of SB and AB. It follows that

$$\Phi(\lambda_0, v) = \Phi_{SB}[\lambda_0(1+\frac{v}{c})^{-1},\ c+v] - \Phi_{AB}[\lambda_0(1+\frac{v}{c})^{-2},\ c] - \Phi_0$$

Φ_{SB} is the phase function of the light ray with path SB, with wavelength $\lambda' = \lambda_0(1+\frac{v}{c})^{-1}$ and velocity $c+v$. Φ_{AB} is the phase function of the *extinction shifted* light with path AB, wavelength $\lambda'' = \lambda_0(1+\frac{v}{c})^{-2}$ and velocity c. Φ_0 is a constant.

We now have the task of determining the relative phase of the light at B as a single function of λ_0 and v. If the light ray SB suffers extinction at B, the scattered light will assume the wavelength $\lambda'' = \lambda_0(1+\frac{v}{c})^{-2}$, since the scattering of the light at the interferometer screen is in principle the same extinction process as a mirror reflection, namely the Lloyd mirror reflection. The scattered light is re-emitted with velocity c. Therefore, at B, the extinction process results in the re-emitted light with a new function Φ_{SB}' of wavelength $\lambda'' = \lambda_0(1+\frac{v}{c})^{-2}$ and propagation velocity c, which is the same function of λ_0 and v

Extinction Shift Theory Applied to Nullified Experiments (Continued)

as the function Φ_{AB} produced by the Lloyd mirror reflection. The new phase function is given by

$$\Phi_{SB}'[\lambda_0(1+\frac{v}{c})^{-2},\ c] \quad .$$

In the vicinity of the screen at distances x such that $x \ll \lambda_0$, the incident light SB is in phase with the reflected light defined by the function Φ_{SB}' for any given point of incidence on the screen. Therefore, at B

$$\Phi_{SB} = \Phi_{SB}' = \Phi_{AB} + \Phi_0$$

and it follows that

$$\Phi(\lambda_0, v) = \Phi_{SB} - \Phi_{AB} - \Phi_0 = constant$$

and consequently

$$\Delta\Phi = \frac{d}{dv}\Phi(\lambda_0, v) = 0.$$

Hence, no fringe shift as a function of v can be observed.

Note: As a consequence of the change in velocity upon mirror reflections and the *extinction shift* of the re-emitted wavelength, an anomalous law-of-reflection relating the angle of incidence θ_i for the wave of velocity $c+v$ and angle of reflection θ_r of the extinguished wave of velocity c is found to be as follows:

$$\frac{Sin\theta_i}{Sin\theta_r} = \frac{c+v}{c} \quad .$$

From the geometry of this experiment using the above relation, it is found that the optical path varies as a function of the velocity v of the source. Fermat's principle requires no variation in the optical path during changes in v.

Extinction Shift Theory Applied to Nullified Experiments (Continued)

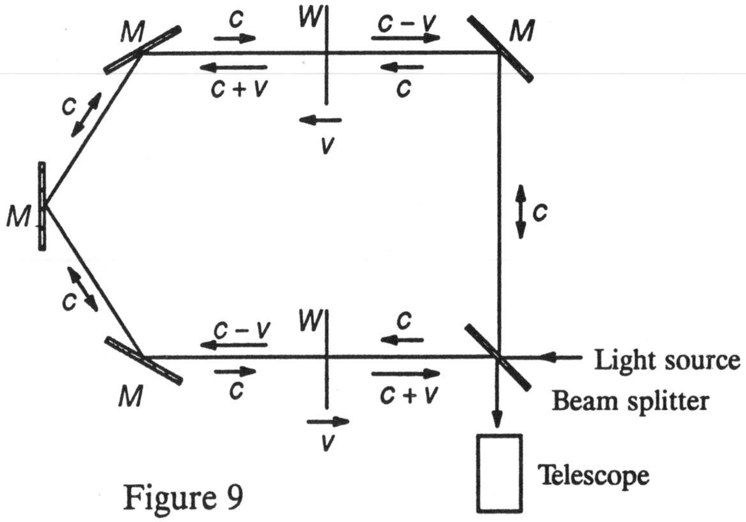

Figure 9

Another type experiment, shown in Figure 9, performed by G. C. Babcock and T. G. Bergman[4], and repeated by P. Beckmann and P. Mandics[5] yielded null results. In this experiment, two windows, which rotate about a common center, absorb the light and re–emit it so that the transit time of the light around the path in the direction of the window motion would decrease and the transit time in the opposite direction would increase.

Fred B. Rotz[6] performed a variation of this time–of–flight experiment using moving slits. J. F. James and R. S. Sternberg[7] used a rotating semicircular disk of glass in an attempt to obtain the transit time differences.

In all of these experiments, the *extinction shift* theory predicts only a second order effect on fringe patterns and wavelengths, as illustrated in the optically equivalent experiment in Figure 8. In the revolving window experiment, each time the light is transmitted by a moving window and then re–emitted by a fixed mirror, the resulting effect on wavelength would be no greater than $\frac{v^2}{c^2}\lambda_0$ as illustrated in Figure 6. Two window transmissions and two mirror reflections would serve only to increase this effect by a factor of 2 which is the equivalent of the rotating window experiment in Figure 9.

Extinction Shift Theory Applied to Nullified Experiments (Continued)

If the velocity of the moving window is such that $\frac{v}{c} = 10^{-7}$, then the *extinction shift* theory predicts a second order effect of $\frac{v^2}{c^2} = 10^{-14}$ for this interferometer. The predicted fringe shift using Doppler methods given by $\frac{2\beta L}{\lambda_o} = 2.9$, where $\beta = 10^{-7}$ and L is the length of the optical path, incorrectly assumes that the transit time change and thus the observed fringe pattern could exhibit changes in the propagation velocity of the *undisturbed* wave. The *undisturbed* wave is not measurable. A fringe shift was not observed in any of these experiments [4,5], thus giving the illusion that the velocity of light is constant in all frames of reference!

Extinction Shift Theory Applied to A. A. Michelson Experiment of 1913

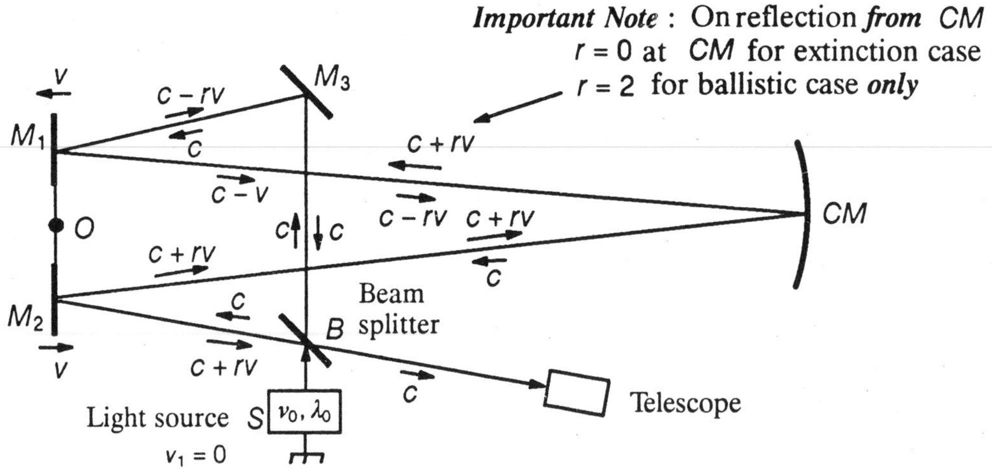

Figure 10

An experiment illustrated in Figure 10 was performed by Albert A. Michelson[8], published in 1913, in order to resolve the question of the ballistic–wave theory. In this experiment, two mirrors M_1 and M_2 were rotated about a common center O, providing moving sources so that the transit time difference in the optical loop is noted for the two possible directions around the loop. An observed fringe shift of the magnitude $\Delta = \frac{v(\tau_1 - \tau_2)}{\lambda} = \frac{kdv}{c\lambda}$ for specific values of k as viewed through the telescope [8], indicating a difference in transit times $\tau_1 - \tau_2$ propagated in the two possible directions, would support a ballistic {tennis ball} theory, re–emission theory or a relativistic theory for $k = 0$, $k = 4$ or $k = 8$ respectively.

Starting from the beam splitter B to the moving mirror M_2, to concave mirror CM, to moving mirror M_1, to the fixed mirror M_3 and back to the beam splitter B, the transit time difference is calculated using the Galilean transformations and the above stated postulates. Also, the frequency and wavelength calculations for the output of the two possible loop directions are noted.

For this apparatus, the distance from O to CM was 6.08 m and the mirror separation M_1 to M_2 was given as 26.5 cm. Thus, the light paths may be considered practically perpendicular to M_1 and M_2. If we assume mechanical symmetry for the apparatus, then the propagation velocities for the two loops are practically as indicated in Figure 10.

Extinction Shift Theory Applied to A. A. Michelson Experiment (Cont.)

Assuming symmetry for the geometry of the experimental apparatus, then the path lengths can be assigned as follows: $B \rightarrow M_2 = M_1 \rightarrow M_3 = s$, $CM \rightarrow M_1 = M_2 \rightarrow CM = d$

and $B \rightarrow M_3 = M_3 \rightarrow B = x$, $\Delta d = \frac{2d}{c} v$

where $\Delta d = \frac{2d}{c} v$ is the moving mirror displacement distance during transit time $\tau = \frac{2d}{c}$.
{ Note again, on reflection ***from*** CM , $r = 0$ for ***extinction*** case! $r = 1$ at moving mirrors.}

Assume also that the velocities v of M_1 and M_3 are practically in the direction of the beams, and that the Galilean transformation holds.

Using the previously derived postulates, the calculated transit times for the respective optical paths are as follows:

Transit time	Loop 1	Loop 2
B to M_2	$\frac{s}{c}$	$\frac{s - \Delta d}{c}(1 + \frac{v}{c})^{-1}$
M_2 to CM	$\frac{d}{c}(1 + \frac{v}{c})^{-1}$	$\frac{d - \Delta d}{c}$
CM to M_1	$\frac{d + \Delta d}{c}$	$\frac{d}{c}(1 - \frac{v}{c})^{-1}$
M_1 to M_3	$\frac{s + \Delta d}{c}(1 - \frac{v}{c})^{-1}$	$\frac{s}{c}$
M_3 to B	$\frac{x}{c}$	$\frac{x}{c}$

The net change in transit time { Loop2 – Loop1 } as function of the velocity v , assuming all optical paths are interference–free, is noted as follows:

$$\Delta\tau = \frac{d}{c}[(1 - \frac{v}{c})^{-1} - (1 + \frac{v}{c})^{-1}] + \frac{s - \Delta d}{c}(1 + \frac{v}{c})^{-1} - \frac{s + \Delta d}{c}(1 - \frac{v}{c})^{-1} - \frac{2\Delta d}{c}$$

$$\Delta\tau = \frac{d}{c}[(1 + \frac{v}{c} + \frac{v^2}{c^2} + ..) - (1 - \frac{v}{c} + \frac{v^2}{c^2} + ..)] + \frac{s - \Delta d}{c}(1 - \frac{v}{c} + \frac{v^2}{c^2} + ..) - \frac{s + \Delta d}{c}(1 + \frac{v}{c} + \frac{v^2}{c^2} + ..) - \frac{2\Delta d}{c}$$

$$\Delta\tau = \frac{2v}{c}(\frac{d}{c} - \frac{s}{c}) - \frac{4dv}{c^2} - \frac{4dv}{c^2}(1 + \frac{v^2}{c^2}) \approx = \frac{2v}{c}(\frac{d}{c} - \frac{s}{c}) - \frac{8dv}{c^2}$$

where $\frac{8dv}{c^2}$ contributes to the net change in transit time $\Delta\tau$ caused by the mirror displacement.

In order for a change in transit time to be noted, due to propagation velocity changes, the primary photons of velocity $c + rv$ { $r = 1$ for re–emission, $r = 2$ for ballistic theory [8] } must survive long enough to be optically registered at the end of the optical path. Also note that air particles may contribute to a transit time effect since they themselves become moving N–ary sources. The *undisturbed* phase difference is $\Delta\phi = \Delta\tau \frac{c}{\lambda} = \frac{2v}{\lambda}(\frac{d}{c} - \frac{s}{c}) - \frac{8dv}{\lambda c}$.

Extinction Shift Theory Applied to A. A. Michelson Experiment (Cont.)

Using the previously derived postulates, the calculated frequencies as perceived at the respective elements { in their reference frames } are as follows:

Frequency	Loop 1	Loop 2
at M_2	$\nu_{M_2} = \nu_0(1+\frac{V}{c})$	at B_2 $\nu_{B_2} = \nu_{M_2} \approx \nu_0(1-2\frac{V^2}{c^2})$
at CM	$\nu_{CM} = \nu_0(1+\frac{V}{c})^2$	at M_2 $\nu_{M_2} = \nu_0(1-\frac{V}{c})^2(1+\frac{V}{c})$
at M_1	$\nu_{M_1} = \nu_0(1+\frac{V}{c})^2(1-\frac{V}{c})$	at CM $\nu_{CM} = \nu_0(1-\frac{V}{c})^2$
at M_3	$\nu_{M_3} = \nu_0(1+\frac{V}{c})^2(1-\frac{V}{c})^2$	at M_1 $\nu_{M_1} = \nu_0(1-\frac{V}{c})$
at B_1	$\nu_{B_1} = \nu_{M_3} \approx \nu_0(1-2\frac{V^2}{c^2})$	at M_3 $\nu_{M_3} = \nu_B = \nu_0$

The net change in frequency as function of the velocity V is noted as follows:

$$\Delta\nu_B = \nu_{B_2} - \nu_{B_1} = \phi$$

Using the previously derived postulates, the calculated *undisturbed* wavelengths at the respective optical paths, as would be noted by the hypothetical observer, are as follows:

Wavelength	Loop 1		Loop 2	
B to M_2	λ_0		$\lambda_0[(1-\frac{V}{c})(1+\frac{V}{c})]^{-2} \approx \lambda_0(1+2\frac{V^2}{c^2})$	
M_2 to CM	$\lambda_0(1+\frac{V}{c})^{-1}$	{*undisturbed*}	$\lambda_0[(1-\frac{V}{c})^2(1+\frac{V}{c})]^{-1}$	{*undisturbed*}
CM to M_1	$\lambda_0(1+\frac{V}{c})^{-2}$		$\lambda_0(1-\frac{V}{c})^{-2}$	
M_1 to M_3	$\lambda_0[(1+\frac{V}{c})^2(1-\frac{V}{c})]^{-1}$	{*undisturbed*}	$\lambda_0(1-\frac{V}{c})^{-1}$	{*undisturbed*}
M_3 to B	$\lambda_0[(1+\frac{V}{c})(1-\frac{V}{c})]^{-2} \approx \lambda_0(1+2\frac{V^2}{c^2})$		λ_0	

The net change in wavelength as function of the velocity V is noted as follows:

$$\Delta\lambda = \lambda_{Loop2} - \lambda_{Loop1} = \phi$$

Thus, there is no frequency or wavelength shift as a result of extinction, and therefore no "fringe motion" registered as a function of velocity V. Note: By extinguishing the *undisturbed* wavelengths by fixed windows or air particles, the outputs will not change since frequency is always passed by any fixed re-emitter or air particles.

Extinction Shift Theory Applied to A. A. Michelson Experiment (Cont.)

Due to the turbulent motion of air medium caused by the rotating windows, it is expected that in the vicinity of the windows, convectional effects or Fresnel drag due to changes in the refractive index of the medium, may contribute to the net transit time effects. At course vacuum pressures, however, it is possible to account for some of the convectional effects. Since the refractive index of air differs from that of vacuum by only 10^{-3} for the short optical paths involved, convection may not factor significantly in the Michelson experiment. At vacuum pressures of not more than 10^{-6} torr, for typical experimental optical paths, any convectional effect on the transit time would be negligible in comparison to the effect due to changes in propagation velocity. Note: The $\frac{8dv}{c^2}$ effect caused by the moving mirror displacement is roughly 4 times the magnitude of the predicted transit time change $\frac{2v}{c}(\frac{d}{c}-\frac{s}{c})$ caused by propagation velocity changes along the *undisturbed path*. The same would hold for the relative phase between the *undisturbed* waves.

It is to be noted that the calculated shift of $\Delta = \frac{v(\tau_1 - \tau_2)}{\lambda} = \frac{4D}{\lambda}(2-r)\frac{v}{c}$ derived by Michelson[8] has an error. Michelson did not apply the $c + rv$ principle properly to all mirror reflections. For the $r = 1$ case, Michelson's phase shift is $\Delta = \frac{4Dv}{\lambda c}$. The correctly calculated shift has an additional term $\frac{2v}{c}(\frac{d}{c}-\frac{s}{c})$ for the change in transit time effect or $\frac{2v}{\lambda}(\frac{d}{c}-\frac{s}{c})$ for the change in phase effect for the $r = 1$ re–emission or *extinction shift* { *undisturbed* } case, a total phase shift of $\Delta\phi = \frac{2v}{\lambda}(\frac{d}{c}-\frac{s}{c}) - \frac{8Dv}{\lambda c}$, which is the combined, but opposing effects of the change in transit time over the *undisturbed* lengths d and s and the mirror displacement effect.

Note: Any observation of this combined effect presumes the paths d and s are *not* totally extinguished! Michelson's experiment was conducted entirely in air. Even in high vacuum (10^{18} to 10^{16} particles per m^3), the probability of survival for *primary* photons at optical wavelengths ($\lambda \approx 5 \cdot 10^{-7}\ m$) over the path of lengths d and s for the dimensions of this apparatus is practically zero. (10^{18} particles per m^3 corresponds to 10^6 particles per m along the path of photons at high vacuum!)

Extinction Shift Theory Applied to A. A. Michelson Experiment (Cont.)

Also note that Michelson's apparatus contains mirrors. The *extinction shift* principle predicts anomalies in the established law of reflection for any changes in the velocities after mirror reflections. It can be easily shown using Galilean transformations that an incident wave front of velocity $c + v$ and angle of incidence θ_i relative to the normal of the mirror surface will reflect with velocity c and with angle of reflection θ_r relative to the normal of the mirror surface according to the relation $\frac{Sin\theta_i}{Sin\theta_r} = \frac{c+v}{c}$. This results in a possible compensating effect at all mirrors.

However, the effect $\Delta = \frac{8Dv}{\lambda c}$ is always observed whether the paths d and s are extinguished or not. Moreover, it is easily shown that the phase shift $\Delta = \frac{8Dv}{\lambda c}$ observed in the Michelson experiment is essentially a Sagnac effect. In the Michelson apparatus, a virtual point source moving on the concave mirror CM of focal length d is the equivalent of a moving reflector that is rigidly attached to M_1 and M_2 since d is practically constant for the movement of the virtual source along the curvature of CM . From the geometry of the apparatus, the area enclosed by M_1 , M_2 and the virtual secondary source at CM , the angular velocity ω and the dimensions of the apparatus, plugged into the Sagnac equation $\Delta = \frac{4A}{\lambda c}\omega$, yields $\frac{4dx}{\lambda c}\omega = \frac{4dv}{\lambda c}$, where x is the radius of rotational motion of the mirrors M_1 and M_2 , ωx is the velocity v . $\frac{8dv}{\lambda c}$ is the combined effect of the clockwise and counter–clockwise paths $M_1 - CM - M_2$ and $M_2 - CM - M_1$. { See also Appendix II on Sagnac effect. }

The Michelson experiment of 1913 should by no means be put in a class of null experiments because it is consistent with the current findings on the calculated transit time effects and the considerations on the moving N–ary sources. The experiment of 1913 did report an optical shift, $\Delta = \frac{v(\tau_1 - \tau_2)}{\lambda} = \frac{kdv}{\lambda c} = 3.76$ fringes, for $k = 8$ and $\frac{v}{c} = 4.6282 \cdot 10^{-8}$ for 1000 rpm moving mirrors, thus discounting the ballistic concept $c + rv$ where $r = 2$ which is consistent with the findings of the *extinction shift* theory where $r = 0$ from fixed mirrors and $r = 1$ from moving mirrors, yielding $\Delta\phi = \frac{2v}{\lambda}(\frac{d}{c} - \frac{s}{c}) - \frac{8Dv}{\lambda c}$ for the *undisturbed* case, and $\Delta\phi = \frac{8Dv}{\lambda c}$ for the *extinguished* case.

Important Note to Optical Experimentalists:

As a consequence of the *extinction shift principle* of *undisturbed* wavelengths, the difference in the number of *undisturbed* waves along the optical paths of the two possible loop directions, noted at a snapshot instant in time, **is not** linearly related to the net transit time difference or to the phase difference between the *undisturbed* waves. The *undisturbed* wavelength **does not** depend on the velocity of the source. Only the net change in transit time and the phase difference between interfering waves are linearly related in all interferometers. The assumption of linearity between wavelength numbers and transit time differences for the Michelson experiment of 1913 and many other well known experiments of equivalent optical path designs is a typical *faux pas* made by many optical experimentalists and has lead to incorrect interpretations of the experimental results.

Conclusion

The *extinction shift principle*, applied to nullified experiments in optics designed to test the theory of the constancy of light velocity, correctly predicts resulting null effects for all these experiments. The absence of first order effects, predicted by using Doppler type principles on the wavelength, frequency and fringe shift calculations, gives merely the illusion that the velocity of light is constant in all frames of reference. The *extinction shift* theory successfully isolates the Sagnac effect, the only phase shift observed in the Albert Michelson experiment of 1913. A first order effect due to changes in propagation velocity of light **does not** exhibit itself as an optical fringe shift as function of moving source velocity, as correctly predicted by the *extinction shift principle*, in these experiments or any experiment of equivalent optical path designs. These experimental observations may be considered to be a validation of the *extinction shift principle*.

References to Appendix

1. Born, M. and Wolf, E., *Principles of Optics*, Pergamon Press, London - New York, 71, 100 - 104 (1975).

2. Jackson, J.D., *Classical Electrodynamics*, John Wiley & Sons, Inc., New York, 512 - 515 (1975).

3. Beckmann, Petr and Mandics, Peter, *Test of the Constancy of the Velocity of Electromagnetic Radiation in High Vacuum*, Radio Sci. J. Res. NBS/USNC/URSI 69D, No. 4, 623 - 628 (1965).

4. Babcock, G.C., and Bergman, T.G., *Determination of the Constancy of the Speed of Light*, J. Opt. Soc. Am. 54, 147 -151 (1964).

5. Beckmann, Petr and Mandics, Peter, *Experiment on the Constancy of the Velocity of Electromagnetic Radiation*, Radio Sci. J. Res. NBS/USNC/URSI 68D, No. 12, 1265 - 1268 (1964).

6. Rotz, Fred B., *New Test of the Velocity of Light Postulate*, Physics Letters 7, No. 4, 252 - 254 (1963).

7. James, J. F., and Sternberg, R.S., *Change in Velocity of Light Emitted by a Moving Source*, Nature 197, 1192 (1963).

8. Michelson, A.A., *Effect of Reflection from a Moving Mirror on the Velocity of Light*, Astrophysics. J., vol. 37, 190 - 193 (1913).

9. Dowdye, E.H., *Extinction Shift; an Alternative to the Doppler Shift Theory*, (Copyrighted work to be published) (1983).

ELEMENTARY MATHEMATICS

CLASSICAL MECHANICS

GALILEAN TRANSFORMATIONS

Galileo Galilei {1564–1642 AD}

"THE SIMPLICITIES OF NATURAL LAWS ARISE THROUGH THE COMPLEXITIES OF THE LANGUAGES WE USE FOR THEIR EXPRESSION."

: Eugene Paul Wigner

"RAFFINIERT IST DER HERR GOTT, ABER BOSHAFT IST ER NICHT!"

< God is slick, but he ain't mean! >

: Albert Einstein

"The velocity of essence is infinity. Now is everywhere simultaneously."

: E. H. Dowdye, Jr.

"Das Wesen pflanzt sich mit unendlicher Geschwindigkeit fort.
Nun ist gleichzeitig überall."

: E. H. Dowdye, Jr.

Extinction Shift Principle: Graphical

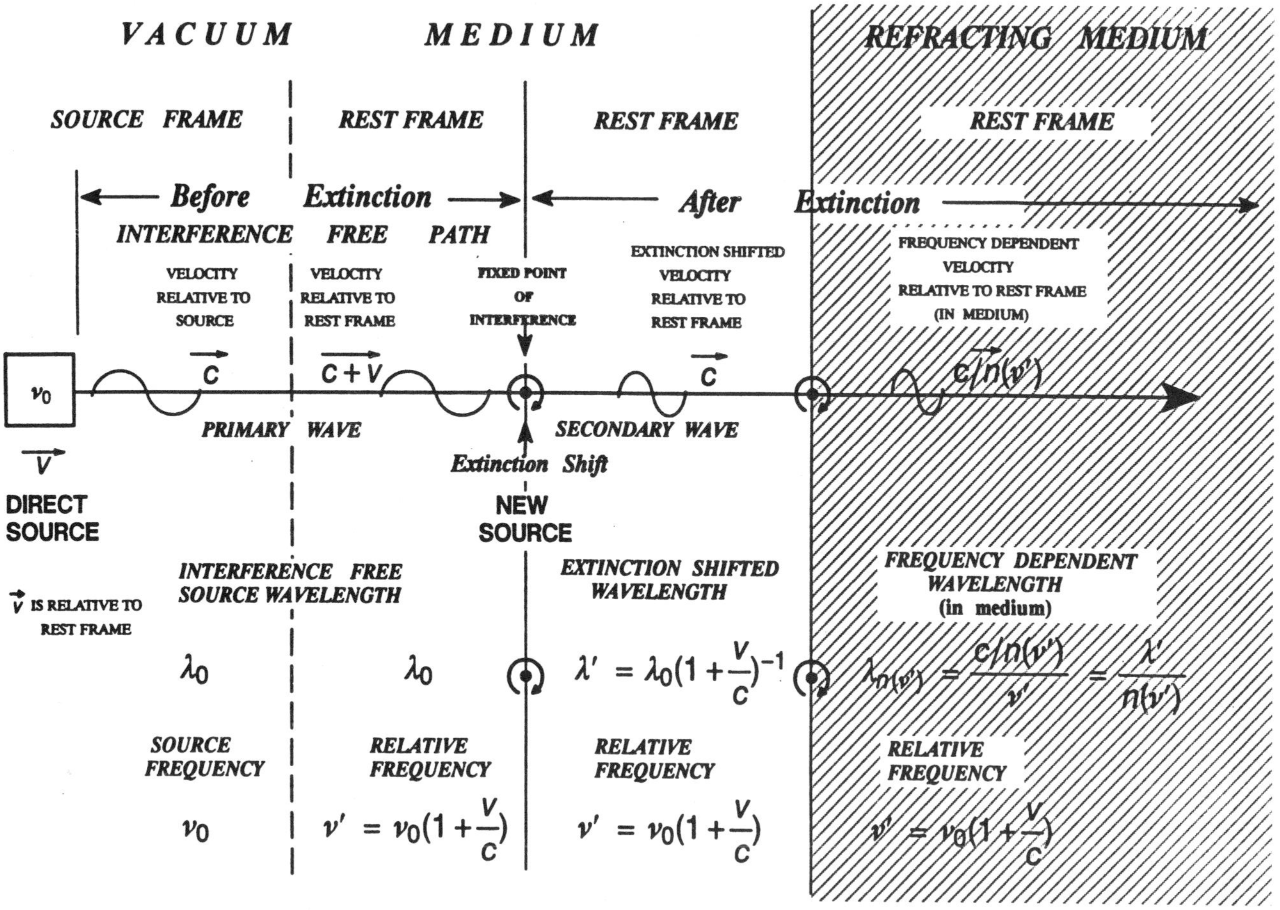